On the Origin and Metamorphoses of Insects

JOHN LUBBOCK

London 1873

TABLE OF CONTENTS

PREFACE

For some years, much of my leisure time has been devoted to the study of the anatomy, development, and habits of the Annulosa, and especially of Insects, on which subjects I have published various memoirs, chiefly in the Transactions of the Royal, Linnæan, and Entomological Societies: of these papers I subjoin a list. Although the details, of which these memoirs necessarily for the most part consist, offer little interest, excepting to those persons who are specially devoted to Entomology, still there are portions which, having reference to the nature of metamorphoses and to the origin of insects, are of a more general character. I have also briefly referred to these questions in a Monograph of the Collembola and Thysanura, recently published by the Ray Society, and in the Opening Address to the Biological Section of the British Association at Brighton in 1872. Under theseviii circumstances, it has been suggested to me that a small volume, containing, at somewhat greater length, in a more accessible form, and with the advantage of illustrations, the conclusions to which I have been led on this interesting subject, might not be altogether without interest to the general reader. The result, which has already appeared in the pages of Nature, is now submitted to the public, with some additions. I am well aware that it has no pretence to be in any sense a complete treatise; that the subject itself is one as to which our knowledge is still very incomplete, and on which the highest authorities are much divided in opinion. Whatever differences of opinion, however, there may be as to the views here put forward, the facts on which they are based will, I believe, be found correct. On this point I speak with the more confidence, on account of the valuable assistance I have received from many friends: to Mr. and Mrs. Busk and Dr. Hooker I am especially indebted.

The papers above referred to are as follows:—

1. On Labidocera.—Annals and Magazine of Natural History, vol. xi., 1853.

2. On Two New Sub-genera of Calanidæ.—Annals and Magazine of Natural History, vol. xii., 1853.

3. On Two New Species of Calanidæ.—Annals and Magazine of Natural History, vol. xii., No. lxvii., 1853.

4. On Two New Species of Calanidæ.—Annals and Magazine of Natural History, vol. xii., No. lxix., 1853.

5. On some Arctic Calanidæ.—Annals and Magazine of Natural History, 1854.

6. On the Freshwater Entomostraca of South America.—Transactions of the Entomological Society, vol. iii., 1855.

7. On some New Entomostraca.—Transactions of the Entomological Society, vol. iv., 1856.

8. On some Marine Entomostraca found at Weymouth.—Annals and Magazine of Natural History, vol. xx., 1857.

9. On the Respiration of Insects.—Entomological Annual, 1857.

10. An Account of the Two Methods of Reproduction in Daphnia.—Transactions of the Royal Society, 1857.

11. On the Ova and Pseudova of Insects.—Transactions of the Royal Society, 1858.

12. On the Arrangement of the Cutaneous Muscles of Pygæra Bucephala.—Linnean Society's Transactions, vol. xxii., 1858.

13. On the Freshwater Entomostraca of South America.—Entomological Society's Transactions, 1858.

14. On Coccus Hesperidum.—Royal Society Proceedings, vol. ix., 1858.

15. On the Distribution of Tracheæ in Insects.—Linnean Society's Transactions, vol. xxiii., 1860.

16. On the Generative Organs and on the Formation of the Egg in Annulosa. Transactions of the Royal Society, 1861.

17. On Sphærularia Bombi.—Natural History Review, 1861.

18. On some Oceanic Entomostraca.—Linnean Society's Transactions, vol. xxiii., 1860.

19. On the Thysanura. Part 1.—Linnean Society's Transactions, 1862.

20. On the Development of Lonchoptera.—Entomological Society's Transactions, 1862.

21. On the Thysanura. Part 2.—Linnean Society's Transactions, 1862.

22. On the Development of Chloëon. Part 1.—Linnean Society's Transactions, 1863.

23. On Two Aquatic Hymenoptera.—Linnean Society's Transactions, 1863.

24. On some little-known Species of Freshwater Entomostraca.—Linnean Society's Transactions, vol. xxiv., 1863.

25. On Sphærularia Bombi.—Natural History Review, 1864.

26. On the Development of Chloëon. Part 2.—Linnean Society's Transactions, 1865.

27. Metamorphoses of Insects.—Journal of the Royal Institution, 1866.

28. On Pauropus.—Linnean Society's Transactions, 1866.

29. On the Thysanura. Part 3.—Linnean Society's Transactions, 1867.

30. Address to the Entomological Society.—Entomological Society's Transactions, 1867.

31. On the Larva of Micropeplus Staphilinoides.—Entomological Society's Transactions, 1868.

32. On the Thysanura. Part 4.—Linnean Society's Transactions, 1869.

33. Addresses to the Entomological Society.—Entomological Society's Transactions, 1867-1868.

34. On the Origin of Insects.—Journal of the Linnean Society, vol. xi.

35. Opening Address to the Biological Section of the British Association.—British Association Report, 1872.

36. Observations on Ants, Bees, and Wasps. Part 1.—Journal of the Linnean Society, 1873.

37. On British Wild Flowers considered in relation to Insects, 1874.

38. Observations on Ants, Bees, and Wasps. Part 2.—Journal of the Linnean Society, 1874.

39. Observations on Ants, Bees, and Wasps. Part 3.—Journal of the Linnean Society, 1875.

40. Observations on Ants, Bees, and Wasps. Part 4.—Journal of the Linnean Society, 1877.

41. On some Points in the Anatomy of Ants.—Quekett Lecture, 1877.—Microscopical Journal.

42. On the Colors of Caterpillars.—Entomological Society's Transactions, 1878.

43. Observations on Ants, Bees, and Wasps. Part 5.—Journal of the Linnean Society, 1878.

44. Observations on Ants, Bees, and Wasps. Part 6.—Journal of the Linnean Society, 1879.

45. On the Anatomy of Ants.—Linnean Society's Transactions, 1880.

46. Observations on Ants, Bees, and Wasps. Part 7.—Journal of the Linnean Society, 1880.

47. Observations on Ants, Bees, and Wasps. Part 8.—Journal of the Linnean Society, 1881.

48. On Fruits and Seeds.—Journal of the Royal Institution, 1881.

49. Observations on Ants, Bees, and Wasps. Part 9.—Journal of the Linnean Society, 1881.

50. On the Limits of Vision among some of the lower Animals.—Journal of the Linnean Society, 1881.

51. Observations on Ants, Bees, and Wasps. Part 10.—Journal of the Linnean Society, 1882.

THE CLASSIFICATION OF INSECTS

About forty years ago the civil and ecclesiastical authorities of St. Fernando in Chili arrested a certain M. Renous on a charge of witchcraft, because he kept some caterpillars which turned into butterflies.1 This was no doubt an extreme case of ignorance; it is now almost universally known that the great majority of insects quit the egg in a state very different from that which they ultimately assume; and the general statement in works on entomology has been that the life of an insect may be divided into four periods.

Thus, according to Kirby and Spence,2 "The states through which insects pass are four: the egg, the larva, the pupa, and the imago." Burmeister,3 also,

says that, excluding certain very rare anomalies, "we may observe four distinct periods of existence in every insect,—namely, those of the egg, the larva, the pupa, and the imago, or perfect insect." In fact, however, the various groups of insects differ widely from one another in the metamorphoses they pass through: in some, as in the grasshoppers and crickets, the changes consist principally in a gradual increase of size, and in the acquisition of wings; while others, as for instance the common fly, acquire their full bulk in a form very different from that which they ultimately assume, and pass through a period of inaction in which not only is the whole form of the body altered, not only are legs and wings acquired, but even the internal organs themselves are almost entirely disintegrated and re-formed. It will be my object, after having briefly described these changes, to throw some light on the causes to which they are due, and on the indications they afford of the stages through which insects have been evolved.

The following list gives the orders or principal groups into which the Class Insecta may be divided. I will not, indeed, here enter upon my own views, but will adopt the system given by Mr. Westwood in his excellent

"Introduction to the Modern Classification of Insects," from which also, as a standard authority, most of the figures on Plates I. to IV., when not otherwise acknowledged, have been taken. He divides insects into thirteen groups, and with reference to eight of them it may be said that there is little difference of opinion among entomologists. These orders are by far the most numerous, and I have

placed them in capital letters. As regards the other five there is still much difference of opinion. It must also be observed that Prof. Westwood omits the parasitic Anoplura, as well as the Thysanura and Collembola.

ORDERS OF INSECTS ACCORDING TO WESTWOOD.

1. Hymenoptera
Bees, Wasps, Ants, andc.
2. Strepsiptera
Stylops, Zenos, andc.
3. Coleoptera
Beetles.
4. Euplexoptera
Earwigs.
5. Orthoptera
Grasshoppers, Crickets, Cockroaches, andc.
6. Thysanoptera
Thrips.
7. Neuroptera
Ephemeras, andc.
8. Trichoptera
Phryganea.
9. Diptera
Flies and Gnats.
10. Aphaniptera
Fleas
11. Heteroptera
Bugs.
12. Homoptera
Aphis, Coccus, andc.
13. Lepidoptera
Butterflies and Moths.

Of these thirteen orders, the eight which I have placed in capital letters—namely the first, third, fifth, seventh, ninth, eleventh, twelfth, and thirteenth, are much the most important in the number and variety of their species; the other five form comparatively small groups. The Strepsiptera are minute insects, parasitic on Hymenoptera: Rossi, by whom they were discovered, regarded them as Hymenopterous; Lamarck placed them among the Diptera; by others they have been considered to be most closely allied to the Coleoptera, but they are now generally treated as an independent order.

The Euplexoptera or Earwigs are only too familiar to most of us. Linnæus classed them among the

Coleoptera, from which, however, they differ in their transformations. Fabricius, Olivier, and Latreille regarded them as Orthoptera; but Dr. Leach, on account of the structure of their wings, considered them as forming the type of a distinct order, in which view he has been followed by Westwood, Kirby, and many other entomologists.

The Thysanoptera, consisting of the Linnæan genus Thrips, are minute insects well known to gardeners, differing from the Coleoptera in the nature of their metamorphoses, in which they resemble the Orthoptera and Hemiptera. The structure of the wings and mouth-parts, however, are considered to exclude them from these two orders.

The Trichoptera, or Caddis worms, offer many points of resemblance to the Neuroptera, while in others they approach more nearly to the Lepidoptera. According to Westwood, the genus Phryganea "forms the connecting link between the Neuroptera and Lepidoptera."

The last of these small aberrant orders is that of the Aphaniptera, constituted for the family Pulicidæ. In their transformations, as in many other respects, they closely resemble the Diptera. Strauss Durckheim indeed said that "la puce est un diptère sans ailes." Westwood, however, regards it as constituting a separate order.

As indicated by the names of these orders, the structure of the wings affords extremely natural and convenient characters by which the various groups may be distinguished from one another. The mouth-parts also are very important; and, regarded from

this point of view, the Insecta have been divided into two series—the Mandibulata and Haustellata, or mandibulate and suctorial groups, between which, as I have elsewhere shown,4 the Collembola (Podura, Smynthurus, andc.) occupy an intermediate position. These two series are:—

Mandibulata.

Haustellata.

Hymenoptera.

Lepidoptera.

Strepsiptera.

Diptera.

Coleoptera.

Aphaniptera.

Euplexoptera.

Hemiptera.

Orthoptera.

Homoptera.

Trichoptera?

Thysanoptera?

Again—and this is the most important from my present point of view—insects have sometimes been divided into two other series, according to the nature of their metamorphoses: "Heteromorpha," to use the terminology of Prof. Westwood,

"or those in which there is no resemblance between the parent and the offspring; and Homomorpha, or those in which the larva resembles the imago, except in the absence of wings. In the former the larva is generally worm-like, of a soft and fleshy consistence, and furnished with a mouth, and often with six short legs attached in pairs to the three segments succeeding the head. In the Homomorpha, including the Orthoptera, Hemiptera, Homoptera, and certain Neuroptera, the body, legs, and antennæ are nearly similar in their form to those of the perfect insect, but the wings are wanting."

Heteromorpha.

Haustellata.

Hymenoptera.

Euplexoptera.

Strepsiptera.

Orthoptera.

Coleoptera.

Hemiptera.

Trichoptera.

Homoptera.

Diptera.

Thysanoptera.

Aphaniptera.

Lepidoptera.

Neuroptera.

But though the Homomorphic insects do not pass through such striking changes of form as the Heteromorphic, and are active throughout life, still it was until within the last few years generally (though erroneously) considered, that in them, as in the Heteromorpha, the life fell into four distinct periods; those of (1) the egg, (2) the larva, characterized by the absence of wings, (3) the pupa with imperfect wings, and (4) the imago, or perfect insect.

I have, however, elsewhere6 shown that there are not, as a matter of fact, four well-marked stages, and four only, but that in many cases the process is much more gradual.

The species belonging to the order Hymenoptera are among the most interesting of insects. To this order belong the gallflies, the sawflies, the ichneumons, and, above all, the ants and bees. We are accustomed to class the Anthropoid apes next to man in the scale of creation, but if we were to judge animals by their works, the chimpanzee and the gorilla must certainly give place to the bee and the ant. The larvæ of the sawflies, which live on leaves, and of the Siricidæ or long-tailed wasps, which feed on wood, are very much like caterpillars,

having three pairs of legs, and in the former case abdominal pro-legs as well: but in the great majority of Hymenoptera the larvæ are legless, fleshy grubs (Plate II., Figs. 7-9); and the various modes by which the females provide for, or secure to, them a sufficient supply of appropriate nourishment constitutes one of the most interesting pages of Natural History.

The species of Hymenoptera are very numerous; in this country alone there are about 3,000 kinds, most of which are very small. In the pupa state they are inactive, and show distinctly all the limbs of the perfect insect, encased in distinct sheaths, and folded on the breast. In the perfect state they are highly organized and very active. The working ants and some few species are wingless, but the great majority have four strong membranous wings, a character distinguishing them at once from the true flies, which have only one pair of wings.

The sawflies are so called because they possess at the end of the body a curious organ, corresponding to the sting of a wasp, but which is in the form of a fine-toothed saw. With this instrument the female sawfly cuts a slit in the stem or leaf of a plant, into which she introduces her egg. The larva much resembles a caterpillar, both in form and habits. To this group belongs the nigger, or black caterpillar of the turnip, which is often in sufficient numbers to do much mischief. Some species make galls, but the greater number of galls are formed by insects of another family, the Cynipidæ.

In the Cynipidæ (Plate I., Fig. 7) the female is provided with an organ corresponding to the saw of the sawfly, but resembling a needle. With this she stings or punctures the surface of leaves, buds, stalks, or even roots of various plants. In the wound thus produced she lays one or more eggs. The effects of this proceeding, and particularly of the irritating fluid which she injects into the wound, is to produce a tumour or gall, within which the egg hatches, and on which the larva, a thick fleshy grub (Plate II., Fig. 7), feeds. In some species each gall contains a single larva; in others, several live together.

The oak supports several kinds of gallflies: one produces the well-known oak-apple, one a small swelling on the leaf resembling a currant, another a gall somewhat like an acorn, another attacks the root; the species making the bullet-like galls, which are now so common, has only existed for a few years in this country; the beautiful little spangles so common in autumn on the under side of oak leaves are the work of another species, the Cynus longipennis. One curious point about this group is, that in some of the commonest species the females alone are known, no one yet having ever succeeded in finding a male.

Another great family of the Hymenoptera is that of the ichneumons; the females lay their eggs either in or on other insects, within the bodies of which the larvæ live. These larvæ are thick, fleshy, legless grubs, and feed on the fatty tissues of their hosts, but do not attack the vital organs. When full-grown, the grubs eat their way through the skin of

the insect, and turn into chrysalides. Almost every kind of insect is subject to the attacks of these little creatures, which are no doubt useful in preventing the too great multiplication of insects, and especially of caterpillars. Some species are so minute that they actually lay their eggs within those of other insects Figs. (15, 16). These parasites assume very curious forms in their larval state.

But of all the Hymenoptera, the group containing the ant, the bee, and the wasp is the most interesting. This is especially the case with the social species, though the solitary ones also are extremely remarkable. The solitary bee or wasp, for instance, forms a cell generally in the ground, places in it a sufficient amount of food, lays an egg, and closes the cell. In the case of bees, the food consists of honey; in that of wasps, the larva requires animal food, and the mother therefore places a certain number of insects in the cell, each species having its own special prey, some selecting small caterpillars, some beetles, some spiders. Cerceris bupresticida, as its name denotes, attacks beetles belonging to the genus Buprestis. Now if the Cerceris were to kill the beetle before placing it in the cell, it would decay, and the young larva, when hatched, would find only a mass of corruption. On the other hand, if the beetle were buried uninjured, in its struggles to escape it would be almost certain to destroy the egg. The wasp has, however, the instinct of stinging its prey in the centre of the nervous system, thus depriving it of motion, and let us hope of suffering, but not of life; consequently, when the young larva leaves

the egg, it finds ready a sufficient store of wholesome food.

Other wasps are social, and, like the bees and ants, dwell together in communities. They live for one season, dying in autumn, except some of the females, which hibernate, awake in the spring, and form new colonies. These, however, do not, under ordinary circumstances, live through a second winter. One specimen which I kept tame through last spring and summer, lived until the end of February, but then died. The larvæ of wasps (Plate II., Fig. 9) are fat, fleshy, legless grubs. When full-grown they spin for themselves a silken covering, within which they turn into chrysalides. The oval bodies which are so numerous in ants' nests, and which are generally called ants' eggs, are really not eggs but cocoons. Ants are very fond of the honey-dew which is formed by the Aphides, and have been seen to tap the

Aphides with their antennæ, as if to induce them to emit some of the sweet secretion. There is a species of Aphis which lives on the roots of grass, and some ants collect these into their nests, keeping them, in fact, just as we do cows. Moreover they collect the eggs in the autumn and tend them through the winter (when they are of no use) with the same care as their own, so as to have a supply of young Aphides in the spring. This is one of the most remarkable facts I know in the whole history of animal life. One species of red ant does no work for itself, but makes slaves of a black kind, which then do everything for their masters. The slave makers will not even put food into their own mouths, but would starve in the midst of plenty, if they had not a slave to feed them. I found, however, that I could keep them in life and health for months if I gave them a slave for an hour or two in a week to clean and feed them.

Ants also keep a variety of beetles and other insects in their nests. That they have some reason for this seems clear, because they readily attack any unwelcome intruder; but what that reason is, we do not yet know. If these insects are to be regarded as the domestic animals of the ants, then we must admit that the ants possess more domestic animals than we do.

Some indeed of these beetles produce a secretion which is licked by the ants like the honeydew; there are others, however, which have not yet been shown to be of any use to the ants, and yet are rarely, if ever, found, excepting in ants' nests.

M. Lespès, who regards these insects as true domestic animals, has recorded[8] some interesting observations on the relations between one of them (Claviger Duvalii) and the ants (Lasius niger) with which it lives. This species of Claviger is never met with except in ants' nests, though on the other hand there are many communities of Lasius which possess none of these beetles; and M. Lespès found that when he placed Clavigers in a nest of ants which had none of their own, the beetles were immediately killed and eaten, the ants themselves being on the other hand kindly received by other communities of the same species. He concludes from these observations that some communities of ants are more advanced in civilization than others; the suggestion is

no doubt ingenious, and the fact curiously resembles the experience of navigators who have endeavoured to introduce domestic animals among barbarous tribes; but M. Lepès has not yet, so far as I am aware, published the details of his observations, without which it is impossible to form a decided opinion. I have sometimes wondered whether the ants have any feeling of reverence for these beetles; but the whole subject is as yet very obscure, and would well repay careful study.

The order Strepsiptera are a small, but very remarkable group of insects, parasitic on bees and wasps. The larva (Pl. IV., Fig. 8) is minute, six-legged, and very active; it passes through its transformations within the body of the bee or wasp. The male and female are very dissimilar. The males are minute, very active, short-lived, and excitable, with one pair of large membranous wings. The females (Pl. III., Fig. 8), on the contrary, are almost motionless, and shaped very much like a bottle; they never quit the body of the bee, but only thrust out the top of the bottle between the abdominal rings of the bee.

In the order Coleoptera, the larvæ differ very much in form. The majority are elongated, active, hexapod, and more or less depressed; but those of the Weevils (Pl. II., Fig. 6), of Scolytus (Pl. II., Fig. 4), andc., which are vegetable feeders, and live surrounded by their food,—as, for instance, in grain, nuts, andc.,—are apod, white, fleshy grubs, not unlike those of bees and ants. The larvæ of the Longicorns, which live inside trees, are long, soft, and fleshy, with six short legs. The Geodephaga, corresponding with the Linnæan genera

Cicindela and Carabus, have six-legged, slender, carnivorous larvæ; those of Cicindela, which waylay their prey, being less active than the hunting larvæ of the Carabidæ. The Hydradephaga, or water-beetles (Dyticidæ and Gyrinidæ), have long and narrow larvæ (Pl. IV., Fig. 6), with strong sickle-shaped jaws, short antennæ, four palpi, and six small eyes on each side of the head; they are very voracious. The larvæ of the Staphylinidæ are by no means unlike the perfect insect, and are found in similar situations; their jaws are powerful, and their legs moderately strong. The larvæ of the Lamellicorn beetles Figs. (1-6)—cockchafers, stag-beetles, andc.—feed on vegetable substances or on dead animal matter. They are long, soft, fleshy grubs, with the abdomen somewhat curved, and generally lie on their side. The larvæ of the Elateridæ, known as wireworms, are long and slender, with short legs. That of the glowworm (Lampyridæ) is not unlike the apterous female. The male glowworm, on the contrary, is very different. It has long, thin, brown wing-cases, and often flies into rooms at night, attracted by the light, which it probably mistakes for that of its mate.

The metamorphoses of the Cantharidæ are very remarkable, and will be described subsequently. The larvæ are active and hexapod. The Phytophaga (Crioceris, Galeruca, Haltica, Chrysomela, andc.) are vegetable feeders, both as larvæ and in the perfect state. The larvæ are furnished with legs, and are not unlike the caterpillars of certain Lepidoptera.

The larva of Coccinella (the Ladybird) is somewhat depressed, of an elongated ovate form, with a

small head, and moderately strong legs. It feeds on Aphides.

Thus, then, we see that there are among the Coleoptera many different forms of larvæ. Macleay considered that there were five principal types.

1. Carnivorous hexapod larvæ, with an elongated, more or less flattened body, six eyes on each side of the head, and sharp falciform mandibles (Carabus, Dyticus, andc.).

2. Herbivorous hexapod larvæ, with fleshy, cylindrical bodies, somewhat curved, so that they lie on their side.

3. Apod grub-like larvæ, with scarcely the rudiments of antennæ (Curculio).

4. Hexapod antenniferous larvæ, with a subovate body, the second segment being somewhat larger than the others (Chrysomela, Coccinella).

5. Hexapod antenniferous larvæ, of oblong form, somewhat resembling the former, but with caudal appendages (Meloë, Sitaris).

The pupa of the Coleoptera is quiescent, and "the parts of the future beetle are plainly perceivable, being encased in distinct sheaths; the head is applied against the breast; the antennæ lie along the sides of the thorax; the elytra and wings are short and folded at the sides of the body, meeting on the under side of the abdomen; the two anterior pairs of legs are entirely exposed, but the hind pair are covered by wing-cases, the extremity of the thigh only appearing beyond the sides of the body."9

In the next three orders—namely, the Orthoptera (grasshoppers, locusts, crickets, walking-stick insects,

cockroaches, andc.), Euplexoptera (earwigs), and Thysanoptera, a small group of insects well known to gardeners under the name of Thrips (Pl. I. and II., Figs. 1 and 2)—the larvæ when they quit the egg already much resemble the mature form, differing, in fact, principally in the absence of wings, which are more or less gradually acquired, as the insect increases in size. They are active throughout life. Those specimens which have rudimentary wings are, however, usually called pupæ.

The Neuroptera present, perhaps, more differences in the character of their metamorphoses than any other order of insects. Their larvæ are generally active, hexapod little creatures, and do not vary from one another in appearance so much, for instance, as those of the Coleoptera, but their pupæ differ essentially; some groups, namely, the Psocidæ, Termitidæ, Libellulidæ, Ephemeridæ, and Perlidæ, remaining active throughout life, like the Orthoptera; while a second division, including the Myrmeleonidæ, Hemerobiidæ, Sialidæ, Panorpidæ, Raphidiidæ, and Mantispidæ, have quiescent pupæ, which, however, in some cases, acquire more or less power of locomotion shortly before they assume the mature state; thus that of Raphidia, though motionless at first, at length acquires strength enough to walk, even while still enclosed in the pupa skin, which is very thin.10

One of the most remarkable families belonging to this order is that of the Termites, or white ants. They abound in the tropics, where they are a perfect pest, and a serious impediment to human development. Their colonies are extremely numerous, and

they attack woodwork and furniture of all kinds, generally working from within, so that their presence is often unsuspected, until it is suddenly found that they have completely eaten away the interior of some post or table, leaving nothing but a thin outer shell. Their nests, which are made of earth, are sometimes ten or twelve feet high, and strong enough to bear a man. One species, Termes lucifugus, is found in the South of France, where it has been carefully studied by Latreille. He found in these communities five kinds of individuals—(1) males; (2) females, which grow to a very large size, their bodies being distended with eggs, of which they sometimes lay as many as 80,000 in a day; (3) a form described by some observers as Pupæ, but by others as neuters. These differ very much from the others, having a long, soft body without wings, but with an immense head, and very large, strong jaws. These individuals act as soldiers, doing apparently no work, but keeping watch over the nest and attacking intruders with great boldness. (4) Apterous, eyeless individuals, somewhat resembling the winged ones, but with a larger and more rounded head; these constitute the greater part of the community, and, like the workers of ants and bees, perform all the labour, building the nest and collecting food. (5) Latreille mentions another kind of individual which he regards as the pupa, and which resembles the workers, but has four white tubercles on the back, where the wings afterwards make their appearance. There is still, however, much difference of opinion among entomologists, with reference to the true nature of these different classes of individuals. M.

Lespès, who has recently studied the same species, describes a second kind of male and a second kind of female, and the subject, indeed, is one which offers a most promising field for future study.

Another interesting family of Neuroptera is that of the Ephemeræ, or Mayflies (Pl. III., Fig. 1), so well known to fishermen. The larvæ (Pl. IV., Fig. 1) are semi-transparent, active, six-legged little creatures, which live in water; having at first no gills, they respire through the general surface of the body. They grow rapidly and change their skin every few days. After one or two moults they acquire seven pairs of branchiæ, or gills, which are generally in the form of leaves, one pair to the segment. When the larvæ are about half grown, the posterior angles of the two posterior thoracic segments begin to elongate. These elongations become more and more marked with every change of skin. One morning, in the month of June, some years ago, I observed a full-grown larva, which had a glistening appearance, owing to the presence of a film of air under the skin. I put it under the microscope, and, having added a drop of water with a pipette, looked through the glass. To my astonishment, the insect was gone, and an empty skin only remained. I then caught a second specimen, in a similar condition, and put it under the microscope, hoping to see it come out. Nor was I disappointed. Very few moments had elapsed, when I had the satisfaction of seeing the thorax open along the middle of the back; the two sides turned over; the insect literally walked out of itself, unfolded its wings, and in an instant flew up to the window. Several times since, I have had the pleasure of witnessing this marvellous change, and it is really wonderful how rapidly it takes place: from the moment when the skin first cracks, not ten seconds are over before the insect has flown away.

Another family of Neuroptera, the Dragon-flies, or Horse-stingers, as they are sometimes called, from a mistaken idea that they sting severely enough to hurt a horse, though in fact they are quite harmless, also spend their early days in the water. The larvæ are brown, sluggish, ugly creatures, with six legs. They feed on small water-animals, for which they wait very patiently, either at the bottom of the water, or on some aquatic plant. The lower jaws are attached to a long folding rod; and when any unwary little creature approaches too near the larva, this apparatus is shot out with such velocity that the prey which comes within its reach seldom escapes. In their perfect condition, also, Dragon-flies feed on other insects, and may often be seen hawking round ponds. The so-called Ant-lions in many respects resemble the Dragon-flies, but the habits of the larvæ are very dissimilar. They do not live in the water, but prefer dry places, where they bury themselves in the loose sand, and seize with their long jaws any small insect which may pass. The true Ant-lion makes itself a round, shallow pit in loose ground or sand, and buries itself at the bottom. Any inattentive little insect which steps over the edge of this pit immediately falls to the bottom, and is instantaneously seized by the Ant-lion. Should the insect escape, and attempt to climb up the side of the pit, the Ant-lion is said to throw sand at it, knocking it down again.

One other family of Neuroptera which I must

mention, is the Hemerobiidæ. The perfect insect is a beautiful, lace-winged, very delicate, green creature, something like a tender Dragon-fly, and with bright, green, touching eyes. The female deposits her eggs on leaves, not directly on the plant itself, but attached to it by a long white slender footstalk. The larva has six legs and powerful jaws, and makes itself very useful in destroying the Hop-fly.

The insects forming the order Trichoptera are well known in their larval condition, under the name of caddis worms. These larvæ are not altogether unlike caterpillars in form, but they live in water—which is the case with very few lepidopterous larvæ—and form for themselves cylindrical cases or tubes, built up of sand, little stones, bits of stick, leaves, or even shells. They generally feed on vegetable substances, but will also attack minute freshwater animals. When full grown, the larva fastens its case to a stone, the stem of a plant, or some other fixed substance, and closes the two ends with an open grating of silken threads, so as to admit the free access of water, while excluding enemies. It then turns into a pupa which bears some resemblance to the perfect insect, "except that the antennæ, palpi, wings, and legs are shorter, enclosed in separate sheaths, and arranged upon the breast." The pupa remains quiet in the tube until nearly ready to emerge, when it comes to the surface, and in some cases creeps out of the water. It is not therefore so completely motionless as the pupæ of Lepidoptera.

The Diptera, or Flies, comprise insects with two wings only, the hinder pair being represented by minute club-shaped organs called "haltères." Flies quit the egg generally in the form of fat, fleshy, legless grubs. They feed principally on decaying animal or vegetable matter, and are no doubt useful as scavengers. Other species, as the gadflies, deposit their eggs on the bodies of animals, within which the grubs feed, when hatched. The mouth is generally furnished with two hooks which serve instead of jaws. The pupæ of Diptera are of two kinds. In the true flies, the outer skin of the full-grown larva is not shed, but contracts and hardens, thus assuming the appearance of an oval brownish shell or case, within which the insect changes into a chrysalis. The pupæ of the gnats, on the contrary, have the limbs distinct and enclosed in sheaths. They are generally inactive, but some of the aquatic species continue to swim about.

One group of Flies, which is parasitic on horses, sheep, bats, and other animals, has been called the Pupipara, because it was supposed that they were not born until they had arrived at the condition of pupæ. They come into the world in the form of smooth, ovate bodies, much resembling ordinary dipterous pupæ, but as Leuckart has shown,11 they are true, though abnormal, larvæ.

The next order, that of the Aphaniptera, is very small in number, containing only the different species of Flea. The larva is long, cylindrical, and legless; the chrysalis is motionless, and the perfect insect is too well known, at least, as regards its habits, to need any description.

The Heteroptera, unlike the preceding orders of insects, quit the egg in a form differing from that of the perfect insect principally in the absence of wings, which are gradually acquired. In their metamorphoses they resemble the Orthoptera, and are active through life. The majority are dull in colour, though some few are very beautiful. The species constituting this group, though very numerous, are generally small, and not so familiarly known to us as those of the other large orders, with indeed one exception, the well-known Bug. This is not, apparently, an indigenous insect, but seems to have been introduced. The word is indeed used by old writers, but either as meaning a bugbear, or in a general sense, and not with reference to this particular insect. In this country it never acquires wings, but is stated to do so sometimes in warmer climates. The Heteroptera cannot exactly be said either to sting or bite. The jaws, of which, as usual among insects, there are two pairs, are like needles, which are driven into the flesh, and the blood is then sucked up the lower lip, which has the form of a tube. This peculiar structure of the mouth prevails throughout the whole order; consequently their nutriment consists almost entirely of the juices of animals or plants. The Homoptera agree with the Heteroptera in the structure of the mouth, and in the metamorphoses. They differ principally in the front wings, which in Homoptera are membranous throughout, while in the Heteroptera, the front part is thickened and leathery. As in the Heteroptera, however, so also in the Homoptera, some species do not acquire wings. The Cicada, celebrated for its chirp, and the lanthorn fly, belong to this group. So also does the so-called Cuckoo-spit, so common in our gardens, which has the curious

faculty of secreting round itself a quantity of frothy fluid which serves to protect it from its enemies. But the best known insects of this group are the Aphides or Plant-lice; while the most useful belong to the Coccidæ, or scale insects, from one species of which we obtain the substance called lac, so extensively used in the manufacture of sealing-wax and varnish. Several species also have been used in dyeing, especially the Cochineal insect of Mexico, a species which lives on the cactus. The male Coccus is a minute, active insect, with four large wings; while the female, on the contrary, never acquires wings, but is very sluggish, broad, more or less flattened, and in fact, when full grown, looks like a small brown, red, or white scale.

The larva of the order Lepidoptera are familiar to us all, under the name of caterpillars. The insects of this order in their larval condition are almost all phytophagous, and are very uniform both in structure and in habits. The body is long and cylindrical, consisting of thirteen segments; the head is armed with powerful jaws; the three following segments, the future prothorax, mesothorax, and metathorax, each bears a pair of simple articulated legs. Of the posterior segments, five also bear false or pro-legs, which are short, unjointed, and provided with a number of hooklets. A caterpillar leads a dull and uneventful life; it eats ravenously, and grows rapidly, casting its skin several times during the process, which generally lasts only a few weeks; though in some cases, as for instance that of the goat-moth, it extends over a period of two or three years, after which the larva changes into a quiescent pupa or chrysalis.

THE INFLUENCE OF EXTERNAL CONDITIONS

On the form and structure of larvæ.

The facts recapitulated briefly in the preceding chapter show, that the forms of insect larvæ depend greatly on the group to which they belong. Thus the same tree may harbour larvæ of Diptera, Hymenoptera, Coleoptera, and Lepidoptera; each presenting the form typical of the family to which it belongs.

If, again, we take a group, such, for instance, as the Lamellicorn beetles, we shall find larvæ extremely similar in form, yet very different in habits. Those, for instance, of the common cockchafer (Fig. 1) feed on the roots of grass; those of Cetonia aurata (Fig. 2) inhabit ants' nests; the larvæ of the genus Trox (Fig. 3) are found on dry animal substances; of Oryctes (Fig. 4) in tan-pits; of Aphodius (Fig. 5) in dung; of Lucanus (the stag-beetle, Fig. 6) in wood.

On the other hand, in the present chapter it will be my object to show that the form of the larva depends very much on the conditions of its life. Thus, those larvæ which are internal parasites, whether in animals

or plants, are vermiform, as are those which live in cells, and depend on their parents for food. On the other hand, larvæ which burrow in wood have strong jaws and generally somewhat weak thoracic legs; whilst those which feed on leaves have the thoracic legs more developed, but less so than the carnivorous species. Now, the Hymenoptera, as a general rule, belong to the first category: the larvæ of the Ichneumons, andc., which live in animals,—those of the Cynipidæ, inhabiting galls,—and those of ants, bees, wasps, andc., which are fed by their parents, are fleshy, apodal grubs; though the remarkable fact that the embryos of bees in one stage of their development possess rudiments of thoracic legs which subsequently disappear, seems to show, not indeed that the larvæ of bees were ever hexapod, but that bees are descended from ancestors which had hex

apod larvæ, and that the present apod condition of these larvæ is not original, but results from their mode of life.

On the other hand, the larvæ of Sirex (Fig. 14) being wood-burrowers, possess well-developed thoracic legs. Again, the larvæ of the Tenthredinidæ, which feed upon leaves, closely resemble the caterpillars of Lepidoptera, even to the presence of abdominal pro-legs.

The larvæ of most Coleoptera (Beetles) are active, hexapod, and more or less flattened: but those which live inside vegetable tissues, such as the weevils, are apod fleshy grubs, like those of Hymenoptera. Pl. II., Fig. 6, represents the larva of the nut-weevil, Balaninus (Pl. I., Fig. 6), and it will be seen that it closely resembles Pl. II., Fig. 5, which represents that of a fly (Anthrax), Pl. I., Fig. 5, and Pl. II., Figs. 7, 8, and 9, which represent respectively those of a Cynips or gall-fly (Pl. I., Fig. 7), an ant (Pl. I., Fig. 8), and wasp (Pl. I., Fig. 9). Nor is Balaninus the only genus of Coleoptera which affords us examples of this fact. Thus in the genus Scolytus (Pl. I., Fig. 4), the larvæ (Pl. II., Fig. 4), which, as already mentioned, feed on the bark of the elm, closely resemble those just described, as also do those of Brachytarsus (Fig. 7). On the other hand, the larvæ of certain beetles feed on

leaves, like the caterpillars of Lepidoptera; thus that of Crioceris Asparagi (Fig. 8)—which, as its name denotes, feeds on the asparagus—closely resembles the larvæ of certain Lepidoptera, as for instance of Thecla spini. From this point of view the transformations of the genus Sitaris (Pl. III., Fig. 4), which have been very carefully investigated by M. Fabre, are peculiarly interesting.12

The genus Sitaris (a small beetle allied to Cantharis, the blister-fly, and to Meloë, the oil-beetle) is parasitic on a kind of Bee (Anthophora), which excavates subterranean galleries, each leading to a cell. The eggs of the Sitaris, which are deposited at the entrance of these galleries, are hatched at the end of September or beginning of October; and M. Fabre not

unnaturally expected that the young larvæ, which are active little creatures with six serviceable legs (Fig. 9), would at once eat their way into the cells of the Anthophora. No such thing: till the month of April following they remain without leaving their birthplace, and consequently without food; nor do they in this long time change either in form or size. M. Fabre ascertained this, not only by examining the burrows of the Anthophoras, but also by direct observation of some young larvæ kept in captivity. In April, however, his captives at last awoke from their long lethargy, and hurried anxiously about their prisons. Naturally inferring that they were in search of food, M. Fabre supposed that this would consist either of the larvæ or pupæ of the Anthophora, or of the honey with which it stores its cell. All three were tried without success. The first two were neglected, and the larvæ, when placed on the latter, either hurried away, or perished in the attempt, being evidently unable to deal with the sticky substance. M. Fabre was in despair: "Jamais expérience," he says, "n'a éprouvé pareille déconfiture. Larves, nymphes, cellules, miel, je vous ai tous offert; que voulez-vous donc, bestioles maudites?" The first ray of light came to him from our countryman, Newport, who ascertained that a small parasite found by Léon Dufour on one of the wild bees, and named by him Triungulinus, was, in fact, the larva of Meloë;. The larvæ of Sitaris much resembled Dufour's Triungulinus; and acting on this hint, M. Fabre examined many specimens of Anthophora, and found on them at last the larvæ of his Sitaris. The males of Anthophora emerge from the

pupæ sooner than the females, and M. Fabre ascertained that, as they come out of their galleries, the little Sitaris larvæ fasten upon them. Not, however, for long: instinct teaches them that they are not yet in the straight path of development; and, watching their opportunity, they pass from the male to the female bee. Guided by these indications, M. Fabre examined several cells of the Anthophora: in some, the egg of the Anthophora floated by itself on the surface of the honey; in others, on the egg, as on a raft, sat the still more minute larva of the Sitaris. The mystery was solved. At the moment when the egg is laid the Sitaris larva springs upon it. Even while the poor mother is carefully fastening up her cell, her mortal enemy is beginning to devour her offspring: for the egg of the Anthophora serves not only as a raft, but as a repast. The honey which is enough for either, would be too little for both; and the Sitaris, therefore, at its first meal, relieves itself from its only rival. After eight days the egg is consumed, and on the empty shell the Sitaris undergoes its first transformation, and makes its appearance in a very different form, as shown in Fig. 10.

The honey which was fatal before is now necessary; the activity which before was necessary is now useless; consequently, with the change of skin, the active, slim larva changes into a white, fleshy grub, so organized as to float on the surface of the honey, with the mouth beneath, and the spiracles above the surface: "grâce à l'embonpoint du ventre," says M. Fabre, "la larve est à l'abri de l'asphyxie." In this state it remains until the honey is consumed; then the

animal contracts, and detaches itself from its skin, within which the further transformations take place. In the next stage, which M. Fabre calls the pseudo-chrysalis (Fig. 11), the larva has a solid corneous envelope and an oval shape; and in its colour, consistency, and immobility reminds one of a Dipterous pupa. The time passed in this condition varies much. When it has elapsed, the animal moults again, again changes its form, and assumes that shown in Fig. 12; after this it becomes a pupa (Fig. 13) without any remarkable peculiarities. Finally, after these wonderful changes and adventures, in the month of August the perfect Sitaris (Pl. III., Fig. 4) makes its appearance.

On the other hand, there are cases in which larvæ diverge remarkably from the ordinary type of the group to which they belong, without, as it seems in our present imperfect state of information, any sufficient reason.

Thus the ordinary type of Hymenopterous larva, as we have already seen, is a fleshy apod grub; although those of the leaf-eating and wood-boring groups, Tenthredinidæ and Siricidæ (Fig. 14), are caterpillars, more or less closely resembling those of Lepidoptera. There is, however, a group of minute Hymenoptera, the larvæ of which reside within the eggs or larvæ of other insects. It is difficult to understand why these larvæ should differ from those of Ichneumons, which are also parasitic Hymenoptera, and should be, as will be seen by the accompanying figures, of such remarkable and grotesque forms. The first known of these curious larvæ was observed by De Filippi,13 who,

having collected some of the transparent eggs of a small Beetle (Rhynchites betuleti), to his great surprise found more than half of them attacked by a parasite, which proved to be the larva of a minute Hymenopterous insect belonging to the Pteromalidæ. Fig. 15 shows the egg of the Beetle, with the parasitic larva, which is represented on a larger scale in Fig. 16.

More recently this group has been studied by M. Ganin,14 who thus describes the development of Platygaster. The egg, as in allied Hymenopterous families, for instance in Cynips, is elongated and club-shaped (Fig. 17). After a while a large nucleated cell appears in the centre (Fig. 18). This nucleated cell divides (Fig. 19) and subdivides. The outermost cells continue the same process, thus forming an outer investing layer. The central, on the contrary, enlarges considerably, and develops within itself a number of daughter cells (Figs. 20 and 21), which gradually form a mulberry-like mass, thus giving rise to the embryo (Fig. 22).

Ganin met with the larvæ of Platygaster in those of a small gnat, Cecidomyia. Sometimes as many as fifteen parasites occurred in one gnat, but as a rule only one of these attained maturity. The three species of Platygaster differ considerably in form, as shown in Figs. 23-25. They creep about within the larva of Cecidomyia by means of the strong hooked feet, kf, somewhat aided by movements of the tail. They possess a mouth, stomach, and muscles, but the nervous, vascular, and respiratory systems do not make their appearance until later. After some time the larva (Fig. 23) changes its skin, assuming the form represented in Fig. 26. In this moult the last abdominal segment of the first larva is entirely thrown off: not merely the outer skin, as in the case of the other segments, but also

the hypodermis and the muscles. This larva, as will be seen by the figure, resembles a barrel or egg in form, and is .870 mm. in length, the external appendages having disappeared, and the segments being indicated only by the arrangement of the muscles. slkf is the œsophagus leading into a wide stomach which occupies nearly the whole body, gsae is the rudiment of the supra-œsophageal ganglia, bsm the ventral nervous cords. The ventral nervous mass has the form of a broad band, with straight sides; it consists of embryonal cells, and remains in this undeveloped condition during the whole larval state.

At the next moult the larva enters its third state, which, as far as the external form (Fig. 27) is concerned, differs from the second only in being somewhat more elongated. The internal organs, however, are much more complex and complete. The tracheæ have made their appearance, and the mouth is provided with a pair of mandibles. From this point the metamorphoses of Platygaster do not appear to differ materially from those of other parasitic Hymenoptera.

An allied genus, Polynema, has also very curious larvæ. The perfect insect is aquatic in its habits, swimming by means of its wings; flying, if we may say so, under water.15 It lays its eggs inside those of Dragon-flies; and the embryo, as shown in Fig. 28, has the form of a bottle-shaped mass of undifferentiated embryonal cells, covered by a thin cuticle, but without any trace of further organization. Protected by the egg-shell of the Dragon-fly, and bathed in the nourishing fluid of the Dragon-fly's egg, the young Polynema imbibes nourishment through its whole surface, and increases rapidly in size. The digestive canal gradually makes its appearance; the cellular mass forms a new skin beneath the original cuticle, distinctly divided into segments, and provided with certain appendages. After a while the old cuticle is thrown off, and the larva gradually assumes the form shown in Fig. 29. The subsequent metamorphoses of Polynema offer no special peculiarities.

From these facts—and, if necessary, many more of the same nature might have been brought forward—it seems to me evident that while the form of any given larva depends to a certain extent on the group of insects to which it belongs, it is also greatly influenced by the external conditions to which it is subjected; that it is a function of the life which the larva leads and of the group to which it belongs.

The larvæ of insects are generally regarded as being nothing more than immature states—as stages in the development of the egg into the imago; and this might more especially appear to be the case with those insects in which the larvæ offer a general resemblance in form and structure (excepting of course so far as relates to the wings) to the perfect insect. Nevertheless we see that this would be a very incomplete view of the case. The larva and pupa undergo changes which have no relation to the form which the insect will ultimately assume. With a general tendency to this goal, as regards size and the development of the wings, there are coincident other changes having reference only to existing wants and condition. Nor is there in this, I think, anything which need surprise us. External circumstances act on the insect in its preparatory states, as well as in its perfect condition. Those who believe that animals are susceptible of great, though gradual, change through the influence of external conditions, whether acting, as Mr. Darwin has suggested, through natural selection, or in any other manner, will see no reason why these changes should be confined to the mature animal. And it is evident that creatures which, like the majority of insects, live during the successive periods of their existence in very different circumstances, may undergo considerable changes in their larval organization, in consequence of forces acting on them while in that condition; not, indeed, without affecting, but certainly without affecting to any corresponding extent, their ultimate form.

I conclude, therefore, that the form of the larva in insects, whenever it departs from the hexapod

Campodea type, has been modified by the conditions under which it lives. The external forces acting upon it are different from those which affect the mature form; and thus changes are produced in the young which have reference to its immediate wants, rather than to its final form.

And, lastly, as a consequence, that metamorphoses may be divided into two kinds, developmental and adaptional or adaptive.

ON THE NATURE OF METAMORPHOSES

In the preceding chapters we have considered the life history of insects after they have quitted the egg; but it is obvious that to treat the subject in a satisfactory manner we must take the development as a whole, from the commencement of the changes in the egg, up to the maturity of the animal, and not suffer ourselves to be confused by the fact that insects leave the egg in very different stages of embryonal development. For though all young insects when they quit the egg are termed "larvæ," whatever their form may be (the case of the so-called Pupipara not constituting a true exception), still it must be remembered that some of these larvæ are much more advanced than others. It is evident that the larva of a fly, as regards its stage of development, corresponds in reality neither with that of a moth nor with that of a grasshopper. The maggots of flies, in which the appendages of the head are rudimentary, belong to a lower grade than the grubs of bees, andc., which have antennæ, mandibles, maxillæ,
labrum, labium, and, in fact, all the mouth parts of a perfect insect.
The caterpillars of Lepidoptera are generally classed with the vermiform larva of Diptera and Hymenoptera, and contrasted with those of Orthoptera, Hemiptera, andc.; but, in truth, the possession of thoracic legs places them, together with the similar larvæ of the Tenthredinidæ, on a decidedly higher level. Thus, then, the period of growth (that in which the animal eats and increases in size) occupies sometimes one stage in the development of an insect, sometimes another; sometimes, as for instance in the case of Chloëon, it continues through more than one; or, in other words, growth is accompanied by development. But, in fact, the question is even more complicated than this. It is not only that the larvæ of insects at their birth offer the most various grades of development, from the grub of a fly to the young of a grasshopper or a cricket; but that, if we were to

classify larvæ according to their development, we should have to deal, not with a simple case of gradations only, but with a series of gradations, which would be different according to the organ which we took as our test.

Apart, however, from the adaptive changes to which special reference was made in the previous chapter, the differences which larvæ present are those of gradation, not of direction. The development of a grasshopper does not pursue a different course from that of a butterfly, but the embryo attains a higher state before quitting the egg in the former than in the latter: while in most Hymenoptera, as for instance in Bees, Wasps, Ants, andc., the young are hatched

without thoracic appendages; in the Orthoptera, on the contrary, the legs are fully developed before the young animal quits the egg.

Prof. Owen,16 indeed, goes so far as to say that the Orthoptera and other Homomorphous insects are, "at one stage of their development, apodal and acephalous larvæ, like the maggot of the fly; but instead of quitting the egg in this stage, they are quickly transformed into another, in which the head and rudimental thoracic feet are developed to the degree which characterizes the hexapod larvæ of the Carabi and Petalocera."

I quite believe that this may have been true of such larvæ at an early geological period, but the fact now appears to be, so far at least as can be judged from the observations yet recorded, that the legs of those larvæ which leave the egg with these appendages generally make their appearance before the body-walls have closed, or the internal organs

have approached to completion. Indeed, when the legs first appear, they are merely short projections, which it is not always easy to distinguish from the segments themselves. It must, however, be admitted, that the observations are neither so numerous, nor in most cases so full, as could be wished.

Again in Aphis, the embryology of which has been so well worked out by Huxley,18 the case is very similar, although the legs are somewhat later in making their appearance. When the young was 1/140th of an inch in length, he found the cephalic portion of the embryo beginning, he says, "to extend upwards again over the anterior face of the germ, so as to constitute its anterior and a small part of its superior wall. This portion is divided by a median fissure into two lobes, which play an important part

in the development of the head, and will be termed the 'procephalic lobes.' I have already made use of this term for the corresponding parts in the embryos of Crustacea. The rudimentary thorax presents traces of a division into three segments; and the dorso-lateral margins of the cephalic blastoderm, behind the procephalic lobes, have a sinuous margin. It is in embryos between this and 1/100th of an inch in length, that the rudiments of the appendages make their appearance; and by the growth of the cephalic, thoracic, and abdominal blastoderm, curious changes are effected in the relative position of those regions."

In Chrysopa oculata, one of the Hemerobiidæ, Packard has described19 and figured a stage in which the body segments have made their appearance, but in which he says "there are no indications of limbs. The primitive band is fully formed, the protozorites being distinctly marked, the transverse impressed lines indicating the primitive segments being distinct, and the median furrow easily discerned." Here also, again, the dorsal walls are incomplete, and the internal organs as yet unformed.

In certain Dragon-flies (Calepteryx), and Hemiptera (Hydrometra), the legs, according to Brandt,20 appear at a still earlier stage.

According to the observations of Kölliker,21 it would appear that in the Coleopterous genus Donacia the segments and appendages appear simultaneously.

Kölliker himself, however, frankly admits that "meæ de hoc insecto observationes satis sunt manca," and it is possible that he may never have met with an embryo in the state immediately preceding the appearance of the legs; especially as it appears from the observations of Kowalevski that in Hydrophilus the appendages do not make their appearance until after the segments.22

On the whole, as far as we can judge from the observations as yet recorded, it seems that in Homomorphous insects the ventral wall is developed and divided into segments, before the appearance of the legs; but that the latter are formed almost simultaneously with the cephalic appendages, and before either the dorsal walls of the body or the internal organs.

As it is interesting, from this point of view, to compare the development of other Articulata with that of insects, I give a figure (Fig. 32), representing an early stage in the development of a spider (Pholcus) after Claparède,23 who says, "C'est à ce

moment qu'a lieu la formation des protozonites ou segments primordiaux du corps de l'embryon. Le rudiment ventral s'épaissit suivant six zônes disposées transversalement entre le capuchon anal et le capuchon céphalique."

Among Centipedes the development of Julus has been described by Newport.24 The first period, from the deposition of the egg to the gradual bursting of the shell, and exposure of the embryo within it, which, however, remains for some time longer in connection with the shell, lasts for twenty-five days. The segments of the body, originally six in number, make their appearance on the twentieth day after the deposition of the egg, at which time there were no traces of legs. The larva, when it leaves the egg, is a soft, white, legless grub (Fig. 33), consisting of a head and seven segments, the head being somewhat firmer in texture than the rest of the body. It exhibits rudimentary antennæ, but the legs are still only represented by very slight papilliform processes

on the undersides of the segments to which they belong.

As already mentioned, it is possible that at one time the vermiform state of the Homomorphous insects—which, as we have seen, is now so short, and passed through at so early a stage of development—was more important, more prolonged, and accompanied by a more complete condition of the internal organs. The compression, and even disappearance of those embryonal stages which are no longer adapted to the mode of life—which do not benefit the animal—is a phenomenon not without a parallel in other parts of the animal or even of the vegetable kingdom. Just as in language long compound words have a tendency to concision, and single letters sometimes linger on, indicating the history of a word, like the "l" in "alms," or the "b" in "debt," long after they have ceased to influence the sound; so in embryology useless stages, interesting as illustrations of past history, but without direct advantage under present conditions, are rapidly passed through, and even, as it would appear, in some cases altogether omitted.

For instance, among the Hydroida, in the great majority of cases, the egg produces a body more or less resembling the common Hydra of our ponds, and known technically as the "trophosome," which develops into the well-known Medusæ or jelly-fishes. The group, however, for which Prof. Allman has proposed the term Monopsea,25 and of which the genus Ægina may be taken as the type, is, as he says, distinguished by the absence of a hydriform stage, "the ovum becoming developed through direct metamorphosis into a medusiform body, just as in the other orders it is developed into a hydriform body." Fig. 34 represents, after Allman, a colony of Bougainvillea fruticosa of the natural size. It is a British species, which is found growing on buoys, floating timber, andc., and, says Allman,26 "when in health and vigour, offers a spectacle unsurpassed in interest by any other species—every branchlet crowned by its graceful hydranth and budding with

Medusæ in all stages of development (Fig. 35), some still in the condition of minute buds, in which no trace of the definite Medusa-form can yet be detected; others, in which the outlines of the Medusa can be distinctly traced within the transparent ectothèque (external layer); others, again, just casting off this thin outer pellicle, and others completely freed from it, struggling with convulsive efforts to break loose from the colony, and finally launched forth in the full enjoyment of their freedom into the surrounding water. I know of no form in which so many of the characteristic features of a typical hydroid are more finely expressed than in this beautiful species."

On the other hand, there are groups in which the Medusiform stage becomes less and less important.

The great majority of the higher Crustacea go through well-marked metamorphoses. Figs. 37 and 38 represent two stages in the development of the prawn. In the first (Fig. 37), representing the young animal as it quits the egg, the body is more or less oval and unsegmented; there is a median frontal eye, and three pairs of natatory feet, the first pair simple, while the two posterior are two-branched. Very similar larvæ occur in various other groups of Crustacea. They were at first regarded as mature

forms, and O. F. Müller gave them the name of Nauplius. So also, the second or Zoëa form (Fig. 38) was at first supposed to be a mature animal, until its true nature was discovered by Vaughan Thompson.

The Zoëa form of larva differs from the perfect prawn or crab in the absence of the middle portion of the body and its appendages. The mandibles have no palpi, the maxillipeds or foot-jaws are used as feet, whereas in the mature form they serve as jaws. Branchiæ are either wanting or rudimentary, respiration being principally effected through the walls of the carapace. The abdomen and tail are destitute of articulate appendages. The development of Zoëa into the perfect animal has been well described by Mr. Spence Bate[27] in the case of the common crab (Carcinus mænas).

All crabs, as far as we know, with the exception of a species of land crab (Gegarcinus), described by Westwood, pass through a stage more or less resembling that shown in Fig. 38. On the other hand, the great group of Edriopthalma, comprising Amphipoda (shore-hoppers, andc.) and Isopoda (wood-lice, andc.) pass through no such metamorphosis; the development is direct, as in the Orthoptera. It is true that one species, Tanais Dulongii, though a typical Isopod in form and general character, is said to retain in some points, and especially in the mode of respiration, some peculiarities of the Zoëa type; but this is quite an exceptional case. In Mysis, says F. Müller,[28] "there is still a trace of the Nauplius stage; being

transferred back to a period when it had not to provide for itself, the Nauplius has become degraded into a mere skin; in Ligia this larva-skin has lost the traces of limbs, and in Philoscia it is scarcely demonstrable."

The Echinodermata in most cases "go through a very well-marked metamorphosis, which often has more than one larval stage.... The mass of more or less differentiated sarcode, of which the larva, or pseud-embryo, as opposed to the Echinoderm within it, is made up, always carries upon its exterior certain bilaterally-arranged ciliated bands, by the action of which the whole organism is moved from place to place; and it may be strengthened by the super-addition to it of a framework of calcareous rods."[29] Müller considered that the mouth and pharynx of the larva were either absorbed or cast off with the calcareous rods, but were never converted into the corresponding organs of the perfect Echinoderm. According to A. Agassiz, however, this is not the case, but on the contrary "the whole larva and all its appendages are gradually drawn into the body, and appropriated."[30]

As this process continues, the little creature gradually loses its power of swimming, and, sinking to the bottom, looses the bands of ciliæ, and attaches itself by its base to some stone or other solid substance, the knob of the club being free. The calcareous framework increases in size, and the expanded head forms itself into a cup, round which from five to fifteen delicate tentacles, as shown in Fig. 44, make their appearance.

In this stage the young animal resembles one of the stalked Crinoids, a family of Echinoderms very abundant in earlier geological periods, but which has almost disappeared, being, as we see, now represented by the young states of existing more advanced, free, species. This attached, plant-like condition of Comatula was indeed at first supposed to be a mature form, and was named Pentacrinus; but we now know that it is only a stage in the development of Comatula. The so-called Pentacrinus increases considerably in size, and after various gradual changes, which time does not now permit me to describe, quits the stalk, and becomes a free Comatula.

The metamorphoses of the Starfishes are also very remarkable. Sars discovered, in the year 1835, a curious little creature about an inch in length, which he named Bipinnaria asterigera (Figs. 45-47), and which he then supposed to be allied to the ciliograde Medusæ. Subsequent observations, however, made in 1844, suggested to him that it was the larva of a Starfish, and in 1847 MM. Koren and Danielssen satisfied themselves that this was the case.

But while certain Starfishes thus go through metamorphoses similar in character, and not less remarkable than those of sea-eggs, there are others—as, for instance, the genus Asteracanthion—in which development may be said to be direct—the organs and appendages special to the Pseudembryo being in abeyance; while in another genus, Pteraster, they are reduced to a mere investing membrane.35

Among the Ophiurans also we find two well-marked types of development. Some passing through metamorphoses, while others, as for instance Ophiopholis bellis, "is developed very much after the method of Asteracanthion Mülleri, without passing through the Plutean stage."36

Even in the same species of Echinoderm the degree of development attained by the larva differs to a certain extent according to the temperature, the supply of food, andc. Thus in Comatula, specimens which are liberally supplied with sea-water, and kept warm, hurry as it were through their early stages, and the free larva becomes distorted by the growing Pentacrinus (see Fig. 43), almost before it has attained its perfect form. On the other hand, under less favourable conditions, if the temperature is low and food less abundant, the early stages are prolonged, the larva is longer lived, and reaches a much higher degree of independent development. Similar differences occur in the development of other animals, as for instance, in the Hydroids,37 and among the insects themselves, in Flies;38 and it is obvious that these facts throw much light on the nature and origin of the metamorphoses of insects, which subject we shall now proceed to consider.

ON THE ORIGIN OF METAMORPHOSES

The question still remains, Why do insects pass through metamorphoses? Messrs. Kirby and Spence tell us they "can only answer that such is the will of the Creator;"39 this, however, is a general confession of faith, not an explanation of metamorphoses. So indeed they themselves appear to have felt; for they immediately proceed to make a suggestion. "Yet one reason," they say, "for this conformation may be hazarded. A very important part assigned to insects in the economy of nature, as we shall hereafter show, is that of speedily removing superabundant and decaying animal and vegetable matter. For such agents an insatiable voracity is an indispensable qualification, and not less so unusual powers of multiplication. But these faculties are in a great degree incompatible; an insect occupied in the work of reproduction could not continue its voracious feeding. Its life, therefore, after leaving the egg, is divided into three stages."

But there are some insects—as, for instance, the

Aphides—which certainly are not among the least voracious, and which grow and breed at the same time. There are also many scavengers among other groups of animals—such, for instance, as the dog, the pig, and the vulture—which undergo no metamorphosis.

It is certainly true that, as a general rule, growth and reproduction do not occur together; and it follows, almost as a necessary consequence, that in such cases the first must precede the second. But this has no immediate connection with the occurrence of metamorphoses. The question is not, why an insect does not generally begin to breed until it has ceased to grow, but why, in attaining to its perfect form, it passes through such remarkable changes; why these changes are so sudden and apparently violent; and why they are so often closed by a state of immobility—that of the chrysalis or pupa; for undoubtedly the quiescent and death-like condition of the pupa is one of the most remarkable phenomena of insect-metamorphoses.

In the first place, it must be observed that many animals which differ considerably in their mature state, resemble one another more nearly when young. Thus birds of the same genus, or of closely allied genera, which, when mature, differ much in colour, are often very similarly coloured when young. The young of the lion and the puma are often striped, and the fœtal Black whale has teeth, like its ally the Sperm whale.

In fact, the great majority of animals do go through well-marked metamorphoses, though in many cases they are passed through within the egg, and thus do

not come within the popular ken. "La larve," says, Quatrefages, "n'est qu'un embryon à vie indépendante."40 Those naturalists who accept in any form the theory of evolution, consider that "the embryonal state of each species reproduces more or less completely the form and structure of its less modified progenitors."41 "Each organism," says Herbert Spencer,42 "exhibits within a short space of time a series of changes which, when supposed to occupy a period indefinitely great, and to go on in various ways instead of one way, give us a tolerably clear conception of organic evolution in general."

The naturalists of the older school do not, as Darwin and Fritz Müller have already pointed out, dispute these facts, though they explain them in a different manner—generally by the existence of a supposed tendency to diverge from an original type. Thus Johannes Müller says, "The idea of development is not that of mere increase of size, but that of progress from what is not yet distinguished, but which potentially contains the distinction in itself, to the actually distinct. It is clear that the less an organ is developed, so much the more does it approach the type, and that during its development it acquires more and more peculiarities. The types discovered by comparative anatomy and developmental history must therefore agree." And again, "What is true in this idea is, that every embryo at first bears only the

type of its section, from which the type of the class, order, andc., is only afterwards developed." Agassiz also observes that "the embryos of different animals resemble each other the more the younger they are."

There are, no doubt, cases in which the earlier states are rapidly passed through, or but obscurely indicated; yet we may almost state it as a general proposition, that either before or after birth animals undergo metamorphoses. The state of development of the young animal at birth varies immensely. The kangaroo (Macropus major), which attains a height of seven feet ten inches, does not when born exceed one inch and two lines in length; the chick leaves the egg in a much more advanced condition than the thrush; and so, among insects, the young cricket is much more highly developed, when it leaves the egg, than the larva of the fly or of the bee;

and, as I have already mentioned, differences occur even within the limit of one species, though not of course to anything like the same extent.

In oviparous animals the condition of the young at birth depends much on the size of the egg: where the egg is large, the abundant supply of nourishment enables the embryo to attain a high stage of development; where the egg is small, and the yolk consequently scanty, the embryo requires an additional supply of food before it can do so. In the former case the embryo is more likely to survive; but when the eggs are large, they cannot be numerous, and a multiplicity of germs may be therefore in some circumstances a great advantage. Even in the same species the development of the egg presents certain differences.43

The metamorphoses of insects depend then primarily on the fact that the young quit the egg at a more or less early stage of development; and that consequently the external forces, acting upon them in this state, are very different from those by which they are affected when they arrive at maturity.

Hence it follows that, while in many instances mature forms, differing greatly from one another, arise from very similar larvæ, in other cases, as we have seen, among some the parasitic Hymenoptera, insects agreeing closely with one another, are produced from larvæ which are very unlike. The same phenomenon occurs in other groups. Thus, while in many cases very dissimilar jelly-fishes arise from almost identical Hydroids, we have also the reverse of the proposition in the fact that in some species, Hydroids of an entirely distinct character produce very similar Medusæ.44

We may now pass to the second part of our subject: the apparent suddenness and abruptness of the changes which insects undergo during metamorphosis. But before doing so I must repeat that these changes are not always, even apparently, sudden and great. The development of an Orthopterous insect, say a grasshopper, from its leaving the egg to maturity, is so gradual that the ordinary nomen clature of entomological works (larva state and pupa state) does not apply to it; and even in the case of Lepidoptera, the change from the caterpillar to the chrysalis and from this to the butterfly is in reality less rapid than might at first sight be supposed; the internal organs are metamorphosed very gradually, and even the sudden and striking change in external form is very deceptive, consisting merely of a throwing off of the outer skin—the drawing aside, as it were of a curtain and the revelation of a form which, far from being new, has been in preparation for days; sometimes even for months.

Swammerdam, indeed, supposed (and his view was adopted by Kirby and Spence) that the larva contained within itself "the germ of the future butterfly, enclosed in what will be the case of the pupa, which is itself included in three or more skins, one over the other, that will successively cover the larva." This was a mistake; but it is true that, if a larva be examined shortly before it is full grown, the future pupa may be traced within it. In the same manner, if we examine a pupa which is about to disclose the butterfly, we find the future insect, soft indeed and imperfect, but still easily recognizable, lying more or less loosely within the pupa-skin.

One important difference between an insect and a vertebrate animal is, that whereas in the latter—as, for instance, in ourselves—the muscles are attached to an internal bony skeleton, in insects no such skeleton exists. They have no bones, and their muscles are attached to the skin; whence the necessity for the hard and horny dermal investment of insects, so different from the softness and suppleness of our own skin. The chitine, or horny substance, of which the outside of an insect consists, is formed by a layer of cells lying beneath it, and, once secreted, cannot be altered. From this the result is, that without a change of skin, a change of form is impossible. In some cases, as for instance in Chloëon, each change of skin is accompanied by a change of form, and thus the perfect insect is gradually evolved. In others, as in caterpillars, several changes of skin take place without any material alteration of form, and the change, instead of being spread over many, is confined to the last two moults.

One explanation of this difference between the larvæ which change their form with every change of skin, and those which do not, is, I believe, to be found in the structure of the mouth. That of the caterpillar is provided with a pair of strong jaws, fitted to eat leaves; and the digestive organs are adapted for this kind of food. On the contrary, the mouth of the butterfly is suctorial; it has a long proboscis, beautifully adapted to suck the nectar from flowers, but which would be quite useless, and indeed only an embarrassment to the larva. The digestive organs also of the butterfly are adapted for the assimilation, not of leaves, but of honey. Now it is evident that if the mouth-parts of the larva were slowly metamorphosed into those of the perfect insect, through a number of small changes, the insect would in the meantime be unable to feed, and liable to perish of starvation in the midst of plenty. In the Orthoptera, and among those insects in which the changes are gradual, the mouth of the so-called larva resembles that of the perfect insect, and the principal difference consists in the presence of wings.

Similar considerations throw much light on the nature of the chrysalis or pupa state—that remarkable period of death-like quiescence which is one of the most striking characteristics of insect metamorphosis. The quiescence of the pupa is mainly owing to the rapidity of the changes going on in it. In that of a butterfly, not only (as has been already mentioned) are the mouth and the digestive organs undergoing change, but the muscles are in a similar state of transition. The powerful ones which move the wings are in process of formation; and even the nervous system, by which the movements are set on foot and regulated, is in a state of rapid change.45

It must not be forgotten that all insects are inactive for a longer or shorter space of time after each moult. The slighter the change, as a general rule, the shorter is the period of inaction. Thus, after the ordinary moult of a caterpillar, the insect only requires a short rest until the new skin is hardened. When, however, the change is great, the period of inaction is correspondingly prolonged. Most pupæ indeed have some slight powers of motion; those which assume the chrysalis state in wood or beneath the ground usually come to the surface when about to assume the perfect state, and the aquatic pupæ of certain Diptera swim about with much activity. Among the Neuroptera, certain families have pupæ as quiescent as those of the Lepidoptera:

others—as, for instance, Raphidia—are quiescent at first, but at length acquire sufficient strength to walk, though still enclosed within the pupa-skin: a power dependent partly on the fact that this skin is very thin. Others again—as, for instance, dragon-flies—are not quiescent on assuming the so-called pupa state for any longer time than at their other changes of skin. The inactivity of the pupa is therefore not a new condition peculiar to this stage, but a prolongation of the inaction which has accompanied every previous change of skin.

Nevertheless the metamorphoses of insects have always seemed to me one of the greatest difficulties of the Darwinian theory. In most cases, the development of the individual reproduces to a certain extent that of the race; but the motionless, imbecile pupa cannot represent a mature form. No one, so far as I know, has yet attempted to explain, in accordance with Mr. Darwin's views, a life-history in which the mouth is first mandibulate and then suctorial, as, for example, in a butterfly. A clue to the difficulty may, I think, be found in the distinction between developmental and adaptive changes; to which I have called attention in a previous chapter. The larva of an insect is by no means a mere stage in the development of the perfect animal. On the contrary, it is subject to the influence of natural selection, and undergoes changes which have reference entirely to its own requirements and condition. It is evident, then, that while the embryonic development of an animal in the egg may be an epitome of its specific history, this is by no means the case with

species in which the immature forms have a separate and independent existence. If an animal which, when young, pursues one mode of life, and lives on one kind of food, subsequently, either from its own growth in size and strength, or from any change of season, alters its habits or food, however slightly, it immediately becomes subject to the action of new forces: natural selection affects it in two different, and, it may be, very distinct manners, gradually tending to changes which may become so great as to involve an intermediate period of change and quiescence.

41

There are, however, peculiar difficulties in those cases in which, as among the Lepidoptera, the same species is mandibulate as a larva, and suctorial as an imago. From this point of view Campodea and the Collembola (Podura, andc.) are peculiarly interesting. There are in insects three principal types of mouth:—

First, the mandibulate;

Secondly, the suctorial; and

Thirdly, that of Campodea and the Collembola generally,

in which the mandibles and maxillæ are retracted, but have some freedom of motion, and can be used for biting and chewing soft substances. This type is, in some respects, intermediate between the other two. Assuming that certain representatives of such a type were placed under conditions which made a suctorial mouth advantageous, those individuals in which the mandibles and maxillæ were best calculated to pierce or prick would be favoured by natural selection, and their power of lateral motion would tend to fall into

abeyance; while, on the other hand, if masticatory jaws were an advantage, the opposite process would take place.

There is yet a third possibility—namely, that during the first portion of life, the power of mastication should be an advantage, and during the second that of suction, or vice versâ. A certain kind of food might abound at one season and fail at another; might be suitable for the animal at one age and not at another. Now in such cases we should have two forces acting successively on each individual, and tending to modify the organization of the mouth in different directions. It cannot be denied that the innumerable variations in the mouth-parts of insects have special reference to their mode of life, and are of some advantage to the species in which they occur. Hence, no believer in natural selection can doubt the possibility of the three cases above suggested, the last of which seems to throw some light on the possible origin of species which are mandibulate in one period of life and not in another. Granting then the transition from the one condition to the other, this would no doubt take place contemporaneously with a change of skin. At such times we know that, even when there is no change in form, the softness of the organs temporarily precludes the insect from feeding for a time, as, for instance, in the case of caterpillars. If, however, any considerable change were involved, this period of fasting must be prolonged, and would lead to the existence of a third condition, that of the pupa, intermediate between the other two. Since the acquisition of wings is a more conspicuous

change than any relating to the mouth, we are apt to associate with it the existence of a pupa-state: but the case of the Orthoptera (grasshoppers, andc.) is sufficient proof that the development of wings is perfectly compatible with permanent activity; the necessity for prolonged rest is in reality much more intimately connected with the change in the constitution of the mouth, although in many cases, no doubt, this is accompanied by changes in the legs, and in the internal organization. An originally mandibulate mouth, however, like that of a beetle, could not, I think, have been directly modified into a suctorial organ like that of a butterfly or a gnat, because the intermediate stages would necessarily be injurious. Neither, on the other hand, for the same reasons, could the mouth of the Hemiptera be modified into a mandibulate type like that of the Coleoptera. But in Campodea and the Collembola we have a type of animal closely resembling certain larvæ which occur both in the mandibulate and suctorial series of insects, possessing a mouth neither distinctly mandibulate nor distinctly suctorial, but constituted on a peculiar type, capable of modification in either direction by gradual change, without loss of utility.

In discussing this subject, it is necessary also to take into consideration the nature and origin of wings. Whence are they derived? why are there normally two pairs? and why are they attached to the meso-and meta-thorax? These questions are as difficult as they are interesting. It has been suggested, and I think with justice, that the wings of insects originally served for aquatic and respiratory purposes.

In the larva of Chloëon (Pl. IV., Fig. 1), for instance, which in other respects so singularly resembles Campodea (Pl. III., Fig. 5), several of the segments are provided with foliaceous expansions which serve as respiratory organs. These so-called branchiæ are in constant agitation, and the muscles which move them in several points resemble those of true wings. It is true that in Chloëon the vibration of the branchiæ is scarcely, if at all, utilized for the purpose of locomotion; the branchiæ are, in fact, placed too far back to act efficiently. The situation of these branchiæ differs in different groups; indeed, it seems probable that originally there were a pair on each segment. In such a case, those branchiæ situated near the centre of the body, neither too much in front nor too far back, would serve the most efficiently as propellers: the same causes which determined the position of the legs would also affect the wings. Thus a division of labour would be effected; the branchiæ on the thorax would be devoted to locomotion; those on the abdomen to respiration. This would tend to increase the development of the thoracic segments, already somewhat enlarged, in order to receive the muscles of the legs.

That wings may be of use to insects under water is proved by the very interesting case of Polynema natans,[46] which uses its wings for swimming. This, however, is a rare case, and it is possible that the principal use of the wings was, primordially, to enable the mature forms to pass from pond to pond, thus securing fresh habitats and avoiding in-and-in breeding. If this were so, the development of wings would gradually have been relegated to a late period of life; and by the tendency to the inheritance of characters at corresponding ages, which Mr. Darwin has pointed out,47 the development of wings would have thus become associated with the maturity of the insect. Thus the late acquisition of wings in the Insecta generally seems to be itself an indication of their descent from a stock which was at one period, if not originally, aquatic, and which probably resembled the present larvæ of Chloëon in form, but had thoracic as well as abdominal branchiæ.

Finally, from the subject of metamorphosis we pass naturally to that most remarkable phenomenon which is known as the "Alternation of Generations:" for the first systematic view of which we are indebted to my eminent friend Prof Steenstrup.48

I have always felt it very difficult to understand why any species should have been created in this double character; nor, so far as I am aware, has any explanation of the fact yet been attempted. Nevertheless insects offer, in their metamorphoses, a phenomenon not altogether dissimilar, and give a clue to the manner in which alternation of generations may have originated. The caterpillar owes its difference from the butterfly to the undeveloped state in which it leaves the egg; but its actual form is mainly due to the influence of the conditions under which it lives. If the cater

pillar, instead of changing into one butterfly, produced several, we should have an instance of alternation of generations. Until lately, however, we knew of no such case among insects; each larva produced one imago, and that not by generation, but by development. It has long been known, indeed, that there are species in which certain individuals remain always apterous, while others acquire wings. Many entomologists, however, regard these abnormal individuals as perfect, though wingless insects; and therefore I shall found no argument upon these cases, although they appear to me deserving of more attention than they have yet received.

Recently, however, Prof. Wagner49 has discovered that, among certain small gnats, the larvæ do not directly produce in all cases perfect insects, but give birth to other larvæ, which undergo metamorphoses of the usual character, and eventually become gnats. His observations have been confirmed, as regards this main fact, by other naturalists; and Grimm has met with a species of Chironomus in which the pupæ lay eggs.50

Here, then, we have a distinct case of alternation of generations, as characterized by Steenstrup. Probably other cases will be discovered in which insects undeniably in the larval state will be found fertile. Nay, it seems to me possible, if not probable, that some larvæ which do not now breed may, in the course of ages, acquire the power of doing so. If this idea is correct, it shows how the remarkable phenomenon,

known as alternation of generations, may have originated.

Summing up, then, the preceding argument, we find among insects various modes of development; from simple growth on the one hand, to well-marked instances of the so-called alternation of generation on the other. In the wingless species of Orthoptera there is little external difference, excepting in size, between the young larva and the perfect insect. The growth is gradual, and there is nothing which would, in ordinary language, be called a metamorphosis. In the majority of Orthoptera, though the presence of wings produces a marked difference between the larva and the imago, the habits are nearly the same throughout life, and consequently the action of external circumstances affects the larva in the same manner as it does the perfect insect.

This is not the case with the Neuroptera. The larvæ do not live under the same conditions as the perfect insects: external forces accordingly affect them in a different manner; and we have seen that they pass through some changes which bear no reference to the form of the perfect insect: these changes, however, are for the most part very gradual. The caterpillars of Lepidoptera have even more extensive modifications to undergo; the mouth of the larva, for instance, being remarkably unlike that of the perfect insect. A change in this organ, however, could hardly take place while the insect was growing fast, and consequently feeding voraciously; nor, even if the change could be thus effected, would the mouth, in its intermediate stages, be in any way fitted

for biting and chewing leaves. The same reasoning applies also to the digestive organs. Hence the caterpillar undergoes little, if any, change, except in size, and the metamorphosis is concentrated, so to say, into the last two moults. The changes then become so rapid and extensive, that the intermediate period is necessarily one of quiescence. In some exceptional cases, as in Sitaris (ante, p. 30) we even find that, the conditions of life not being uniform throughout the larval period, the larva itself undergoes metamorphoses.

Owing to the fact that the organs connected with the reproduction of the species come to maturity at a late period, larvæ are generally incapable of breeding. There are, however, some flies which have viviparous larvæ, and thus offer a typical case of alternation of generations.

Thus, then, we find among insects every gradation, from simple growth to alternation of generations; and see how, from the single fact of the very early period of development at which certain animals quit the egg, we can throw some light on their metamorphoses, and for the still more remarkable phenomenon that, among many of the lower animals, the species is represented by two very different forms. We may even conclude, from the same considerations, that this phenomenon may in the course of ages become still more common than it is at present. As long, however, as the external organs arrive at their mature form before the internal generative organs are fully developed, we have metamorphosis; but if the reverse is the case, then alternation of generations often results.

The same considerations throw much light on the remarkable circumstance, that in alternation of generations the reproduction is, as a general rule, agamic in one form. This results from the fact that reproduction by distinct sexes requires the perfection both of the external and internal organs; and if the phenomenon arise, as has just been suggested, from the fact that the internal organs arrive at maturity before the external ones, reproduction will result in those species only which have the power of agamic multiplication.

Moreover, it is evident that we have in the animal kingdom two kinds of dimorphism.

This term has usually been applied to those cases in which animals or plants present themselves at maturity under two forms. Ants and Bees afford us familiar instances among animals; and among plants the interesting case of the genus Primula has recently been described by Mr. Darwin. Even more recently he has made known to us the still more remarkable phenomenon afforded by the genus Lythrum, in which there are three distinct forms, and which therefore offers an instance of polymorphism.51

The other kind of dimorphism or polymorphism differs from the first in being the result of the differentiating action of external circumstances, not on the mature, but on the young individual. Such different forms, therefore, stand towards one another in the relation of succession. In the first kind the chain of being divides at the extremity; in the other it

is composed of dissimilar links. Many instances of this second form of dimorphism have been described under the name of alternation of generations.

The term, however, has met with much opposition, and is clearly inapplicable to the differences exhibited by insects in various periods of their life. Strictly speaking, the phenomena are frequently not alternate, and in the opinion of some eminent naturalists they are not, strictly speaking, cases of generation at all.52

In order, then, to have some name for these remarkable phenomena, and to distinguish them from those cases in which the mature animal or plant is represented by two or more different forms, I think it would be convenient to retain exclusively for these latter the terms dimorphism and polymorphism; and those cases in which animals or plants pass through a succession of different forms might be distinguished by the name of dieidism or polyeidism.

The conclusions, then, which I think we may draw from the preceding considerations, are:—

1. That the occurrence of metamorphoses arises from the immaturity of the condition in which some animals quit the egg.

2. That the form of the insect larva depends in great measure on the conditions in which it lives. The external forces acting upon it are different

from those which affect the mature form; and thus changes are produced in the young, having refer
ence to its immediate wants, rather than to its final form.

3. That metamorphoses may therefore be divided into two kinds, developmental and adaptional or adaptive.

4. That the apparent abruptness of the changes which insects undergo, arises in great measure from the hardness of their skin, which admits of no gradual alteration of form, and which is itself necessary in order to afford sufficient support to the muscles.

5. The immobility of the pupa or chrysalis depends on the rapidity of the changes going on in it.

6. Although the majority of insects go through three well-marked stages after leaving the egg, still a large number arrive at maturity through a greater or smaller number of slight changes.

7. When the external organs arrive at this final form before the organs of reproduction are matured, these changes are known as metamorphoses; when, on the contrary, the organs of reproduction are functionally perfect before the external organs, or when the creature has the power of budding, then the phenomenon is known as alternation of generations.

ON THE ORIGIN OF INSECTS

"Personne," says Carl Vogt, "en Europe au moins, n'ose plus soutenir la Création indépendante et de toutes pièces des espèces," and though this statement is perhaps not strictly correct, still it is no doubt true, that the Doctrine of Evolution, in some form or other, is accepted by most, if not by all, the greatest naturalists of Europe. Yet it is surprising how much, in spite of all that has been written, Mr. Darwin's views are still misunderstood. Thus Browning, in one of his recent poems, says:—
"That mass man sprang from was a jelly lump Once on a time; he kept an after course Through fish and insect, reptile, bird, and beast, Till he attained to be an ape at last, Or last but one."53
This theory, though it would be regarded by many as a fair statement of his views, is one which Mr. Darwin would entirely repudiate. Whether fish and insect, reptile, bird and beast, are derived from one original stock or not, they are certainly not links in one
sequence. I do not, however, propose to discuss the question of Natural Selection, but may observe that it is one thing to acknowledge that in Natural Selection, or the survival of the fittest, Mr. Darwin has called attention to a vera causa, has pointed out the true explanation of certain phenomena; but it is quite another thing to maintain that all animals are descended from some primordial source.

For my own part, I am satisfied that Natural Selection is a true cause, and, whatever may be the final result of our present inquiries—whether animated nature be derived from one ancestral source, or from many—the publication of the Origin of Species will none the less have constituted an epoch in the History of Biology. But, how far the present condition of living beings is due to that cause; how far, on the other hand, the action of Natural Selection has been modified and checked by other natural laws—by the unalterability of types, by atavism, andc.; how many types of life originally came into being; and whether they arose simultaneously or successively,—these and many other similar questions remain unsolved, even admitting the theory of Natural Selection. All this has indeed been clearly pointed out by Mr. Darwin himself, and would not need repetition but for the careless criticism by which in too many cases the true question has been obscured. Without, however, discussing the argument for and against Mr. Darwin's conclusions, so often do we meet with travesties of it like that which I have just quoted, that it is well worth while to consider the stages through which some group, say for in

stance that of insects, have probably come to be what they are, assuming them to have developed under natural laws from simpler organisms. The question is one of great difficulty. It is hardly necessary to say that insects cannot have passed through all the lower forms of animal life, and naturalists do not at present agree as to the actual line of their development. In the case of insects, the gradual course of evolution through which the present condition of the group has probably been reached, has been discussed by Mr. Darwin, by Fritz Müller, Haeckel, Brauer, myself and others.

In other instances Palæontology throws much light on this question. Leidy has shown that the milk-teeth of the genus Equus resemble the permanent teeth of the ancient Anchitherium, while the milk-teeth of Anchitherium again approximate to the dental system of the still earlier Merychippus. Rütimeyer, while calling attention to this interesting observation, adds that the milk-teeth of Equus caballus in the same way, and still more those of E. fossilis, resemble the permanent teeth of Hipparion.

"If we were not acquainted with the horse," says Flower,[54] "we could scarcely conceive of an animal whose only support was the tip of a single toe on each extremity, to say nothing of the singular conformation of its teeth and other organs. So striking have these characters appeared to many zoologists, that the animals possessing them have been reckoned as an order apart, called Solidungula; but palæon

tology has revealed that in the structure of its skull, its teeth, its limbs, the horse is nothing more than a modified Palæotherium; and though still with gaps in certain places, many of the intermediate stages of these modifications are already known to us, being the Palæotherium, Anchitherium, Merychippus, and Hipparion."

"All Echinoids," says A. Agassiz,[55] "pass, in their early stages, through a condition which recalls to us the first Echinoids which made their appearance in geological ages." On embryological grounds, he observes, we should "place true Echini lowest, then the Clypeastroids, next the Echinolamps, and finally the Spatangoids." Now among the Echinoids of the Trias there are no Clypeastroids, Echinolamps, or Spatangoids. The

Clypeastroids make their appearance in the Lias, the Echinolamps in the Jurassic, while the Spatangoids commence in the Cretaceous period.

Again56 "in the Radiates, the Acalephs in their first stages of growth, that is, in their Hydroid condition, remind us of the adult forms among Polyps, showing the structural rank of the Acalephs to be the highest, since they pass beyond a stage which is permanent with the Polyps; while the Adult forms of the Acalephs have in their turn a certain resemblance to the embryonic phases of the class next above them, the Echinoderms; within the limits of the classes, the same correspondence exists as between the different orders; the embryonic forms of the highest Polyps recall the adult forms of the lower

ones, and the same is true of the Acalephs as far as these phenomena have been followed and compared among them." Indeed, the accomplished authors from whom I have taken the above quotation, do not hesitate to say57 that "whenever such comparisons have been successfully carried out, the result is always the same; the present representatives of the fossil types recall in their embryonic condition the ancient forms, and often explain their true position in the animal kingdom."

Fossil insects are unfortunately rare, there being but few strata in which the remains of this group are well preserved. Moreover, well-characterized Orthoptera and Neuroptera occur as early as the Devonian strata; Coleoptera and Hemiptera in the Coal-measures; Hymenoptera and Diptera in the Jurassic; Lepidoptera, on the contrary, not until the Tertiary. But although it appears from these facts that, as far as our present information goes, the Orthoptera and Neuroptera are the most ancient orders, it is not, I think, conceivable that the latter should have been derived from any known species of the former; on the other hand, the earliest known Neuroptera and Orthoptera, though in some respects less specialized than existing forms, are as truly, and as well characterized, Insects, as any now existing; nor are we acquainted with any earlier forms, which in any way tend to bridge over the gap between them and lower groups, though, as we shall see, there are types yet existing which throw much light on the subject. In the consideration then of this question, we must rely principally on Embryology and Development. I have already referred to the cases in which species, very unlike in their mature condition, are very similar one to another when young. Haeckel, in his "Naturliche Schöpfungsgeschichte," gives a diagram which illustrates this very well as regards Crustacea. Pls. 1-4 show the same to be the case with Insects.

The Stag-beetle, the Dragon-fly, the Moth, the Bee, the Ant, the Gnat, the Grasshopper,—these and other less familiar types seem at first to have little in common. They differ in size, in form, in colour, in habits, and modes of life. Yet the researches of entomologists, following the clue supplied by the illustrious Savigny, have proved, not only that while differing greatly in details, they are constructed on one common plan; but also that other groups, as for instance, Crustacea (Lobsters, Crabs, andc.) and Arachnida (Spiders and Mites), can be shown to be fundamentally similar.

Thus, then, although it can be demonstrated that perfect insects, however much they differ in appearance, are yet reducible to one type, the fact becomes much more evident if we compare the larvæ. M. Brauer[58] and I[59] have pointed out that two types of larvæ, which I have proposed to call Campodea-form and Lindia-form, and which Packard has named Leptiform and Eruciform, run through the principal groups of insects. This is obviously a fact of great importance: as all individual Meloës are derived from a form resembling Pl. II, Fig. 2, it is surely no rash hypothesis to suggest that the genus itself may have been so.

Firstly, however, let me say a word as to the general Insect type. It may be described shortly as consisting of animals possessing a head, with mouth parts, eyes and antennæ; a many segmented body, with three pairs of legs on the segments immediately following the head; with, when mature, either one or two pairs of wings, generally with caudal appendages I will not now enter into a description of their internal anatomy. It will be seen that, except as regards the wings, Pl. IV, Fig. 4, representing the larva of a small beetle named Sitaris, answers very well to this description. Many other Beetles are developed from larvæ closely resembling those of Meloë (Pl. IV, Fig. 2), and Sitaris (Pl. IV, Fig. 4); in fact—except those species the larvæ of which, as, for instance of the Weevils (Pl. II, Fig. 6), are internal feeders, and do not require legs—we may say that the Coleoptera generally are derived from larvæ of this type.

I will now pass to a second order, the Neuroptera. Pl. IV, Fig. 1, represents the larva of Chloëon, a species the metamorphoses of which I described some years ago in the Linnean Transactions,[60] and it is obvious that in essential points it closely resembles the form to which I have just alluded.

The Orthoptera, again, the order to which Grasshoppers, Crickets, Locusts, andc. belong, commence life in a similar condition; and the same may also be said of the Trichoptera.

The larvæ of Bees when they quit the egg are entirely legless, but in an earlier stage they possess well-marked rudiments of thoracic legs, showing, as it seems to me, that their apodal condition is an adaptation to their circumstances. Other Hymenopterous larvæ, those for example of Sirex (Fig. 9), and of the Saw-flies (Fig. 50) have well-developed thoracic legs.

From the difference in external form, and especially from the large comparative size of the abdomen, these larvæ, as well as those of Lepidoptera (Fig. 48),

have generally been classed with the maggots of Flies, Weevils, andc., rather than with the more active form of larva just adverted to. This seems to me, as I have already pointed out,[61] to be a mistake. The caterpillar type differs, no doubt, in its general appearance, owing to its greater clumsiness, but still essentially agrees with that already described.

No Dipterous larva, so far as I know, belongs truly to this type; in fact, the early stages of the pupa in the Diptera seem in some respects to correspond to the larvæ of other Insect orders. The Development of the Diptera is, however, as Weissman62 has shown, very abnormal in other respects.

Thus, then, we find in many of the principal groups of insects that, greatly as they differ from one another in their mature condition, when they leave the egg they more nearly resemble the typical insect type; consisting of a head; a three-segmented thorax, with three pairs of legs; and a many-jointed abdomen, often with anal appendages. Now, is there any mature animal which answers to this description? We need not have been surprised if this type, through which it would appear that insects must have passed so many ages since (for winged Neuroptera have been found in the carboniferous strata) had long ago become extinct. Yet it is not so. The interesting genus Campodea (Pl. III, Fig. 5) still lives; it inhabits damp earth, and closely resembles the larva of Chloëon (Pl. II, Fig. 1), constituting, indeed, a type which, as shown in Pl. 4,

occurs in many orders of insects. It is true that the mouth-parts of Campodea do not resemble either the strongly mandibulate form which prevails among the larvæ of Coleoptera, Orthoptera, Neuroptera, Hymenoptera, Lepidoptera; or the suctorial type of the Homoptera and Heteroptera. It is, however, not the less interesting or significant on that account, since, as I have elsewhere63 pointed out, its mouth-parts are intermediate between the mandibulate and haustellate types; a fact which seems to me most suggestive.

It appears, then, that there are good grounds for considering that the various types of insects are descended from ancestors more or less resembling the genus Campodea, with a body divided into head, thorax, and abdomen: the head provided with mouth-parts, eyes, and one pair of antennæ; the thorax with three pairs of legs; and the abdomen, in all probability, with caudal appendages.

If these views are correct, the genus Campodea must be regarded as a form of remarkable interest since it is the living representative of a primæval type, from which not only the Collembola and Thysanura, but the other great orders of insects have derived their origin.

From what lower group the Campodea type was itself derived is a question of great difficulty. Fritz Müller indeed says,64 "if all the classes of Arthropoda (Crustacea, Insecta, Myriopoda, and Arachnida) are indeed all branches of a common stem (and of this there can scarcely be a doubt), it is evident that

the water-inhabiting and water-breathing Crustacea must be regarded as the original stem from which the other terrestrial classes, with their tracheal respiration, have branched off." Haeckel, moreover, is of the opinion that the Tracheata are developed from the Crustacea, and probably from the Zoëpoda. For my own part, though I feel very great diffidence in expressing an opinion at variance with that of such high authorities, I am rather disposed to suggest that the Campodea type may possibly have been derived from a less highly developed one, resembling the modern Tardigrade,65 a (Fig. 56) smaller and much less highly organized being than Campodea. It possesses two eyes, three anterior pairs of legs, and one at the posterior end of the body, giving it a curious resemblance to some Lepidopterous larvæ.

These legs, however, as will be seen, are reduced to mere projections. But for them, the Tardigrada

would closely resemble the vermiform larva so common among insects. Among Trichoptera the larva early acquires three pairs of legs, but as Zaddach has shown,66 there is a stage, though it is quickly passed through, in which the divisions of the body are indicated, but no trace of legs is yet present. Indeed, there appear to be reasons for considering that while among Crustacea the appendages appear before the segments, in Insects the segments precede the appendages, although this stage of development is very transitory, and apparently, in some cases, altogether suppressed. I say "apparently," because, as I have already mentioned, I am not yet satisfied that it will not eventually be found to be so in all cases. Zaddach, in his careful observations of the embryology of Phryganea, only once found a specimen in this stage, which also, according to the researches of Huxley,67 seems to be little more than indicated in Aphis. It is therefore possible that in other cases, when no such stage has been observed, it not really may be absent, but, from its transitoriness, may have hitherto escaped attention.

Fritz Müller has expressed the opinion68 that this vermiform type is of comparatively recent origin. He says: "The ancient insects approached more nearly to the existing Orthoptera, and perhaps to the wingless Blattidæ, than to any other order, and the complete metamorphosis of the Beetles, Lepidoptera, andc., is of later origin." "There were," he adds, "perfect insects

before larvæ and pupæ." This opinion has been adopted by Mr. Packard69 in his "Embryological Studies on Hexapodous Insects."

M. Brauer70 also considers that the vermiform larva is a more recent type than the Hexapod form, and is to be regarded not as a developmental form, but as an adaptational modification of the earlier active hexapod type. In proof of this he quotes the case of Sitaris.

Considering, however, the peculiar habits of this genus, to which I have already referred, and also that the vermiform type is altogether lower in organization and less differentiated than the Campodea form, I cannot but regard this case as exceptional; one in which the development has been, as it were, to use an expression of Fritz Müller's, "falsified" by the struggle for existence, and which therefore does not truly indicate the successive stages of evolution. On the whole, the facts seem to me to point to the conclusion that, though the grublike larvæ of Coleoptera and some other insects, owe their present form mainly to the influence of external circumstances, and partially also to atavism, still the Campodea type is itself derived from earlier vermiform ancestors. Nicolas Wagner has shown in the case of a small gnat, allied to Cecidomyia, that even now, in some instances, the vermiform larvæ possess the power of reproduction. Such a larva (as, for instance, Fig. 57) very closely resembles some of the Rotatoria, such for instance as Albertia or Notommata, which however

possess vibratile cilia. There is, indeed, one genus—Lindia (Fig. 58)—in which these ciliæ are altogether absent, and which, though resembling Macrobiotus in many respects, differs from that genus in being entirely destitute of legs. I have never met with it myself, but it is described by Dujardin, who found it in a ditch near Paris, as being oblong, vermiform, divided into rings, and terminating posteriorly in two short conical appendages. The jaws are not unlike those of the larvæ of Flies, and indeed many naturalists meeting with such a creature would, I am sure, regard it as a small Dipterous larva; yet

Dujardin figures a specimen containing an egg, and seems to have no doubt that it is a mature form.71

For the next descending stage we must, I think, look among the Infusoria, through such genera as Chætonotus or Ichthydium. Other forms of the Rotatoria, such for instance as Rattulus, and still more the very remarkable species discovered in 1871 by Mr. Hudson,72 and described under the name of Pedalion mira, seem to lead to the Crustacea through the Nauplius form. Dr. Cobbold tells me that he regards the Gordii as the lowest of the Scolecida; Mr. E. Ray Lankester considers some of the Turbellaria, such genera as Mesostomum, Vortex, andc., to be the lowest of existing worms; excluding the parasitic groups. Haeckel73 also regards the Turbellaria as forming the nearest approach to the Infusoria. The true worms seem, however, to constitute a separate branch of the animal kingdom.

We may take, as an illustration of the lower worms, the genus Prorhynchus (Fig. 59), which consists of a hollow cylindrical body, containing a straight simple tube, the digestive organ.

But however simple such a creature as this may be, there are others which are far less complex, far less differentiated; which therefore, on Mr. Darwin's principles, may be considered still more closely to repre

sent the primæval ancestor from which these more highly-developed types have been derived, and which, in spite of their great antiquity—in spite of, or perhaps in consequence of, their simplicity, still maintain themselves almost unaltered.

Thus the form which Haeckel has described74 under the name Protamœba primitiva, Pl. V, Fig. 1-5, consists of a homogeneous and structureless substance, which continually alters its form; putting out and drawing in again more or less elongated processes, and creeping about like a true Amœba, from which, however, Protamœba differs, in the absence of a nucleus. It seems difficult to imagine anything simpler; indeed, as described, it appears to be an illustration of properties without structure. It takes into itself any suitable particle with which it comes in contact, absorbs that which is nutritious, and rejects the rest. From time to time a constriction appears at the centre (Pl. V, Fig. 2), its form approximates more and more to that of an hour-glass (Pl. V, Fig. 3), and at length the two halves separate, and each commences an independent existence (Pl. V, Fig. 5).

In the true Amœbas, on the contrary, we find a differentiation between the exterior and the interior: the body being more or less distinctly divisible into an outer layer and an inner parenchyme. In the Amœbas, as in Protamœba, multiplication takes place by self-division, and nothing corresponding to sexual reproduction has yet been discovered.

Somewhat more advanced, but still of great simplicity, is the Protomyxa aurantiaca (Pl. V, Fig. 8), discovered by Haeckel76 on dead shells of Spirula, where it appears as a minute orange speck, which shows well against the clear white of the Spirula. Examined with a microscope, the speck is seen to be a spherical mass of orange-coloured, homogeneous, albuminous matter, surrounded by a delicate, structureless membrane. It is obvious from this description that these bodies closely resemble eggs, for which indeed Haeckel at first mistook them. Gradually, however, the yellow sphere broke itself up into smaller spherules (Pl. V, Fig. 9), after which the containing membrane burst, and the separate spherules, losing their globular form, crept out as small Amœbæ (Pl. V, Fig. 6), or amœboid bodies. These little bodies moved about, assimilated the minute particles of organic matter, with which they came in contact, and gradually increased in size (Pl. V, Fig. 7) with more or less rapidity according to the amount of nourishment they were able to obtain. They threw out arms in various directions, and if divided each section maintained its individual existence. After a while their movements ceased, they contracted into a ball, and again secreted round themselves a clear structureless envelope.

This completes their life history as observed by Haeckel, who found it easy to retain them in his glasses in perfect health, and who watched them closely.

As another illustration I may take the Magosphæra planula, discovered by Haeckel on the coast of Norway.

In one stage of its existence (Pl. V, Fig. 10) it is a minute mass of gelatinous matter, which continually alters its form, moves about, feeds, and in fact behaves altogether like the Amœba just described. It does not, however, remain always in this condition. After a while it contracts into a spherical form (Pl. V, Fig. ii), and secretes round itself a structureless envelope, which, with the nucleus, gives it a very close resemblance to a minute egg.

Gradually the nucleus divides, and the protoplasm also separates into two spherules (Pl. V, Fig. 12); these two subdivide into four (Pl. V, Fig. 13), and so on (Pl. 5, Fig 14), until at length thirty-two are present, compressed into a more or less polygonal form (Pl. V, Fig. 15). Here this process ends. The separate spherules now begin to lose their smooth outline, to throw out processes, and to show amœboid movements like those of the creatures just described. The processes or pseudopods grow gradually longer, thinner, and more pointed. Their movements become more active, until at length they take the form of ciliæ. The spherical Magosphæra, the upper surface of which has thus become covered with ciliæ, now begins to rotate within the cyst or envelope, which at length gives way and sets free the contained sphere, which

then swims about freely in the water (Pl. V, Fig. 16), thus closely resembling Synura, or one of the Volvocineæ. After swimming about in this condition for a certain time, the sphere breaks up into the separate cells of which it is composed (Pl. V, Fig. 17). As long as the individual cells remained together, they had undergone no changes of form, but after separating they show considerable contractility, and gradually alter their form, until they become undistinguishable from true Amœbæ (Pl. V, Fig. 18). Finally, according to Haeckel, these amœboid bodies, after living for a certain time in this condition, return to a state of rest, again contract into a spherical form, and secrete round themselves a structureless envelope. The life history of some other low organisms, as for instance Gregarina, is of a similar character.

It may be said, and said truly, that the difference between such beings as these and the Campodea, or Tardigrade, is immense. But if it be considered incredible that even during the long lapse of geological time such great changes should have taken place as are implied in the belief that there is genetic connection between them and these lower groups, let us consider what happens under our eyes in the development of each one of these little creatures in the proverbially short space of their individual life.

I will take for instance the first stages, and for the sake of brevity only the first stages, of the life-history of a Tardigrade.77 As shown in Fig. 60, the egg is at first a round body or cell, with a clear central nucleus—the germinal

vesicle; it increases in size, and after a while the yolk and the germinal vesicle divide into two (Fig. 61), then into four (Fig. 62), and so on, just as we have seen to be the case in Magosphæra. From the minute cells (Fig. 63) arising through this process of yolk-segmentation, the body of the Tardigrade is then built up.78

Though I will not now attempt to point out the full bearing of these facts on the study of embryology generally, yet I cannot resist calling attention to the similarity of the development of Magosphœra with the first stages of development of other animals, because it appears to me to possess a significance, the importance of which it would be difficult to overestimate.

Among the Zoophytes Prof. Allman thus describes[79] the process in Laomedea, as representing the Hydroids (Pl. VI, Fig. 1, represents the young egg):—"The first step observable in the segmentation-process is the cleavage of the yolk into two segments (Pl. VI, Fig. 2), immediately followed by the cleavage of these into other two, so that the vitellus is now composed of four cleavage spheres (Pl. VI, Fig. 3)." These spheres again divide (Pl. VI, Fig. 4) and subdivide, thus at length forming minute cells, of which the body of the embryo is built up.

Among the Echinoderms M. Derbès thus describes the first stages (Pl. VI, Figs. 10-13) in the development of the egg of an Echinus (Echinus esculentus):—"Le jaune commence à se segmenter, d'abord en deux, puis en quatre et ainsi de suite, chacune des nouvelles cellules se partageant à son tour en deux."[82] Sars has observed the same thing in the star-fish.[83]

I might have given many other examples, but the above are probably sufficient, and will show that the processes which constitute the life-history of the lowest organized beings very closely resemble the first stages in the development of more advanced groups; that as Allen Thomson has truly observed,[92] "the occurrence of segmentation and the regularity of its phenomena are so constant that we may regard it as one of the best established series of facts in organic nature."

It is true that normal yolk-segmentation is not universal in the animal kingdom; that there are great groups in which the yolk does not divide in this manner,—perhaps owing to some difference in its relation to the germinal vesicle, or perhaps because one of the suppressed stages in embryological development, many examples might be given, not only in zoology, but, as I may state on the authority of Dr. Hooker, in botany also. But, however, this may be, it is surely not uninteresting, nor without significance, to find that changes which constitute the life-history of the lowest creatures for the initial stages even of the highest.

Returning, in conclusion, to the immediate subject of this work, I have pointed out that many beetles and other insects are derived from larvæ closely resembling Campodea.

Since, then, individual insects are certainly in many cases developed from larvæ closely resembling the genus Campodea, why should it be regarded as incredible that insects as a group have gone through similar stages? That the ancestors of beetles under the influence of varying external conditions, and in the lapse of geological ages, should have undergone changes which the individual beetle passes through under our own eyes and in the space of a

few
days, is surely no wild or extravagant hypothesis. Again, other insects come from vermiform larvæ much resembling the genus Lindia, and it has been also repeatedly shown that in many particulars the embryo of the more specialized forms resembles the full-grown representatives of lower types. I conclude, therefore, that the Insecta generally are descended from ancestors resembling the existing genus Campodea, and that these again have arisen from others belonging to a type represented more or less closely by the existing genus Lindia.

Of course it may be argued that these facts have not really the significance which they seem to me to possess. It may be said that when Divine power created insects, they were created with these remarkable developmental processes. By such arguments the conclusions of geologists were long disputed. When God made the rocks, it was tersely said, He made the fossils in them. No one, I suppose, would now be found to maintain such a theory; and I believe the time will come when it will be generally admitted that the structure of the embryo, and its developmental changes, indicate as truly the course of organic development in ancient times as the contents of rocks and their sequence teach us the past history of the earth itself.

FOOTNOTES

1 Darwin's "Researches into the Geology and Natural History of the Countries visited by H.M.S. Beagle," p. 326.

2 Introduction to Entomology, vi. p. 50.

3 Manual of Entomology, p. 30.

4 Linnean Journal, vol. xi.

5 Introduction to the Modern Classification of Insects, p. 17.

6 Linnean Transactions, 1863—"On the Development of Chloëon."

7 The figures on the first four plates are principally borrowed from Mr. Westwood's excellent "Introduction to the Modern Classification of Insects."

8 "Sur la Domestication des Clavigers par les Fourmis." Bull. de la Soc. d'Anthropologie de Paris, 1868, p. 315.

9 Westwood's Introduction, vol. i. p. 36.

10 Westwood's Introduction, vol. ii. p. 52.

11 Die Fortpflanzung und Entwickelung der Pupiparen. Von Dr. R. Leuckart. Halle. 1848.

12 Ann. des Sci. Nat., sér. 4, tome vii. See also Natural History Review, April 1862.

13 Ann. and Mag. of Nat. Hist. 1852.

14 Zeits. für Wiss. Zool. 1869.

15 Transactions of the Linnean Society, 1863.

16 Lectures on the Anatomy, andc. of the Invertebrate Animals.

17 Untersuchungen über die Entwickelung und den Bau der Gliederthiere, 1854.

18 Linnean Transactions, vol. xxii. 1858.

19 "Embryological Studies on Hexapodous Insects." Peabody Academy of Science. Third Memoir.

20 Mém. de l'Acad. Imp. des Sci. de St. Pétersbourg. 1869.

21 Observationes de Prima Insectorum Genesi, p. 14.

22 Mém. de l'Acad. Imp. des Sci. de St. Pétersbourg. tome xvi. 1871, p. 35.

23 Recherches sur l'Evolution des Araignées.

24 Philosophical Transactions, 1841.

25 Monog. of the Gymnoblastic or Tubularian Hydroids. See also Hincks, British Hydroid Zoophytes. Pl. x.

26 Loc. cit. p. 315.

27 Philosophical Transactions, 1859, p. 589.

28 "Facts for Darwin," Eng. Trans. p. 127.

29 Rolleston, "Forms of Animal Life," p. 146.

30 A. Agassiz, "Embryology of the Starfish," p. 25; "Embryology of Echinoderms." Mem. of Am. Ac. of Arts and Sciences N.S. vol. ix. p. 9.

31 Ueber die Gattungen der Seeigellarven. Siebente Abhandlung. Kön. Akad. d. Wiss. zu Berlin. Von Joh. Müller, 1855, Pl. iii. fig. 3.

32 Huxley, Introduction to the Classification of Animals, p. 45.

33 Philosophical Transactions, 1865 and 1866.

34 Loc. cit. Zweit. Abh. Pl. i., figs. 8 and 9.

35 Thomson, on the Embryology of the Echinodermata, Natural History Review, 1863, p. 415. See also Agassiz, "Embryology of the Starfish," p. 62.

36 A. Agassiz, Embryology of Echinoderms, p. 18.

37 Hincks. British Hydroid Zoophytes, pp. 120-147.

38 Zeits. für Wiss. Zool. 1864, p. 228.

39 Introduction to Entomology, 6th ed. vol. i. p. 61.

40 Métamorphoses de l'Homme et des Animaux, p. 133. See also Carpenter, Principles of Physiology. 1851, p. 389.

41 Darwin, Origin of Species, 4th ed. p. 532.

42 Principles of Biology, vi. p. 349.

43 For differences in larva consequent on variation in the external condition, see ante, p. 61.

44 See Hincks. British Hydroid Zoophytes, P. lxii. Agassiz, Sea-side Studies, p. 43.

45 See Newport, Phil. Trans., 1832.

46 Linnean Transactions, 1862.

47 Origin of Species, 4th ed., pp. 14 and 97.

48 On the Alternation of Generations. By J. J. Steenstrup. Trans. by C. Busk, Esq. Ray Society. 1842.

49 Zeit. für Wiss. Zool. 1863.

50 Mém. de l'Acad. Imp. de St. Pétersbourg. vol. xv. 1870.

51 Of course all animals in which the sexes are distinct are in one sense dimorphic.

52 "There is no such thing as a true case of 'alternation of generations in the animal kingdom;' there is only an alternation of true generation with the

totally distinct process of gemmation or fission."—Huxley on Animal Individuality, Ann. and Mag. of Nat. Hist. June 1852.

53 Prince Hohenstiel Schwangau, p. 68.

54 Journal of the Royal Institution. April 1873.

55 "Embryology of Echinoderms," l. c. p. 15.

56 Mr. and Mrs. Agassiz: "Seaside Studies," p. 139.

57 l. c. p. 138.

58 Wien. Zool. Bot. Gesells, 1869.

59 Linnean Transactions, 1863.

60 Linnean Transactions, 1866, vol. xxv.

61 Linnean Transactions, vol. xxiv. p. 65.

62 Siebold und Kolliker's Zeitschr. f. Wiss. Zool., 1864.

63 Linnean Journal, vol. xi.

64 Facts for Darwin, p. 120.

65 A still nearer approach is afforded by the genus Peripatus, which since the above was written has been carefully described, especially by Moseley and Hutton. There are several species, scattered over the southern hemisphere. In general appearance they look like a link between a caterpillar and a centipede. They have a pair of antennæ, two pairs of jaws, and (according to the species) from fourteen to thirty-three pairs of legs. They breathe by means of tracheæ, which open diffusely all over the body.

66 Unters. üb. die Entwick, und den Bau der Gliederthiere, p. 73.

67 Linnean Transactions, v. xxii.

68 Facts for Darwin, trans. by Dallas, p. 118. See also Darwin, "Origin of Species," p. 530. 4th ed.

69 Mem. Peabody Academy of Science, v. I. No, 3.

70 Wien. Zool. Bott. Gesells. 1869, p. 310.

71 See also the descriptions given by Dujardin (Ann. des Sci. Nat. 1851, v. xv.) and Claparède (Anat. und Entwickl. der Wirbel osen Thiere) of the interesting genus Echinoderes, which these two eminent naturalists unite in regarding as intermediate between the Annelides and the Crustacea.

72 "On a New Rotifer." Monthly Microscopical Journal, Sept. 1871.

73 Generelle Morphologie, vol. ii. p. 79.

74 Monographie der Moneren, p. 43.

75 Gegenbaur. Grund. d. Vergleich. Anat. p. 210. See also Dr. M. S. Schultze, Beiträge zur Naturg. der. Turbellarien. 1851. Pl. vi. fig. 1.

76 Monographieder Moneren, p. 10.

77 See Kauffmann, Ueber die Entwickelung and systematische Stellung der Tardigraden. Zeits. f. Wiss. Zool. 1851, p. 220.

78 It is true that among the Insecta generally the first stages of development differ in appearance considerably from those above described; those of Platygaster, as figured by Ganin (ante Figs. 17-22), being very exceptional.

79 Monograph of the Gymnoblastic or Tubularian Hydroids, by G. J.

Allman, Ray Soc. 1871, p. 86.

80 Mém. sur les Vers Intestinaux, 1858.

81 Natural History Review, 1861, p. 44.

82 Ann. des Sci. Nat. 1847, p. 90.

83 Fauna littoralis Norvegiæ, pl. viii.

84 Trans. of the Microsc. Soc. of London, 1851.

85 Quarterly Journal of Microsc. Science, 1853.

86 Wiegmann's Archiv., 1840, p. 196.

87 Ueber die Erzeugung von Schnecken in Holothurier. Berlin, Bericht, 1851. Ann. Nat. Hist. 1852, v. ix. Müller's Archiv., 1852.

88 Natürliche Schöpfungsgeschichte, pl. x.

89 Ann. des Sci. Nat. 1853, p. 89.

90 Ann. des Sci. Nat. 1857, pl. vi.

91 Cyclopædia of Anatomy and Physiology. Art. Ovum, p. 4.

92 Thomson, loc. cit. Article, Ovum, p. 139.

THE END.

www.ingramcontent.com/pod-product-compliance
Lightning Source LLC
Chambersburg PA
CBHW070942180526
45168CB00003B/1145